THE ULTIMATE RETIREMENT ACTIVITY BOOK

Over 100 Activities To Do Now When You're Retired

CHARLIE MILLER

ISBN: 978–1–64845–106–5

Copyright: @ 2023 by LAK Publishing

Contents

Introduction

In 2005, the British actor Patrick MacNee—better known to generations of fans as the suave secret agent John Steed in TV's *The Avengers*—stepped away from Hollywood, and retired after more than 50 years in show business.

"Retirement's the most wonderful thing," he explained at the time. "I get to enjoy all the things I never stopped to notice on the way up. After an extraordinary life, it's time to enjoy my retirement."

And that is precisely what awaits more than one million people in the United States alone every single year: a well-earned, blissfully peaceful retirement!

Retirement is all about making the most of your free time, with an empty diary and a clear horizon ahead. It's a time to look back and celebrate a life's work well done, while looking ahead to many, many more years, filling your days with—well, whatever you want to!

But all this free time raises a good question. Now that your schedule is clear, weekly meetings are a thing of the past, there are no emails and phone calls from the office to fill

up your day, and no need to set your alarm clock for an early start every morning—what exactly are you going to do with all that free time?

Well, happily, this is exactly where this book comes in!

The next 100 pages are chock full of wordsearch puzzles, crossword puzzles, trivia and general knowledge quizzes, curious riddles, words games, picture puzzles, and much, much more.

All of it has been designed to keep you busy in your retirement, and keep your brain ticking over now that the time has come to take a well-earned rest and put your feet up!

Along the way here too, you'll find lots of facts, jokes, inspirational mottos, and famous quotations hopefully to keep you thoroughly entertained, and give you some intriguing food for thought—or both!

So without further ado, let's get things started with the first of our fiendish puzzles...

Puzzles

With retirement in mind, how many of
these re— words can you find in this grid?

```
K N H N H S I L B A T S E E R D Y
R I W K U U I R H H E N D Y E D C
A A L R E R A E P P A E R A O N E
B R U E Y R E W O R K T O E R U T
M T R A R E G R A D E R C R G F A
E S E N O R J I R R B E E E A E U
E E I N R E K T R E R T R F N R L
R R N O E E R E E R W N E O I E A
E E F U C M E W C E E I R R Z I V
E A O N H E T A O E P E N M E N E
N E R C A R I B V N N R G D A V E
A O C E R G R S E T A C U D E E R
C D E M G E E B R E P L A Y A S H
T N Z C E N R E C R E A T E B T F
R E D I C T A T E N I M A X E E R
```

REANNOUNCE REAPPEAR RECHARGE RECOVER RECREATE REDICTATE
REEDUCATE REEMBARK REEMERGE REENACT REENTER REESTABLISH
REEVALUATE REEXAMINE REFORM REFUND REGRADE REINFORCE
REINTER REINVEST REORGANIZE REPLAY RERECORD RERUN RESTRAIN
RETIRE RETRY REWIND REWORK REWRITE

How many retired people does it take to change a lightbulb? Fill in the answers to these quiz questions in the corresponding rows the grid on the right to find out the punchline reading down the shaded column!

1.					
2.					
3.					
4.					
5.					
6.					
7.					
8.					
9.					
10.					
11.					
12.					
13.					

14.					
15.					
16.					
17.					
18.					
19.					
20.					
21.					
22.					
23.					
24.					
25.					
26.					

1. Eugene and Bend are cities in what US state?
2. Which Hollywood actor (surname only) won the Best Actor Oscar for *The Color of Money*?
3. Which Hebrew prophet rode in a chariot of fire?
4. On what sea do Poland and Latvia stand?
5. What is the seventh planet from the sun?
6. What name links the pop stars Swift and James?
7. What is a slanted typeface *like this* known as?
8. What sport does Rafael Nadal play?
9. In the classic horror novel, in what coastal town does Dracula arrive in England?
10. What are there 36 of in a yard?
11. What is the surname of Eurhythmics singer Annie?
12. What is the capital of Portugal?
13. How many "days of Christmas" are there?
14. What is Batman's butler called?
15. The adjective renal relates to what bodily organ?
16. What is Winnie the Pooh's donkey friend called?
17. Who (surname only) was the 33rd US President?
18. Who wrote the famous *Hallelujah* chorus?
19. Moldova is a country on what continent?
20. What was George Washington's wife's name?
21. Who is the patron saint of Scotland?
22. In what English city is St Paul's Cathedral?
23. What was Beethoven's first name?
24. What European capital stands on the river Liffey?
25. Who was the Egyptian god of the underworld?
26. What color are gorse flowers?

All the answers to these clues can be made from the letters of the word RETIREMENT. Can you answer them all?

R E T I R E M E N T

_____ 1. Ant–like creature (7)

_____ 2. Ancient galleon with three banks of oars (7)

_____ 3. Value, excellence (5)

_____ 4. 100cm (5)

_____ 5. Coal worker (5)

_____ 6. Go in again (7)

_____ 7. White stoat (6)

_____ 8. Fingerless glove (6)

_____ 9. Uninspired, cliched (5)

_____ 10. Landlord's leasee (6)

What well known work–related phrase is disguised as the rebus below?

2 ING

WISE WORDS

"To me, retirement means
doing what you have fun doing."
— Dick van Dyke

The answers to the clues on the right here contain **all but one** of the same letters as the clues on the left. Solve the clues, then write this unused letter in the middle circle to spell out—reading down the middle—something you'd best remember for your next vacation. The first set has already been solved for you to give you an idea...

1. Fruit grown in an orchard

APPLE

(P)

Sickly, colorless skin

PALE

2. Direction opposite west

( )

Division of a tennis match

3. Easy, not difficult

( )

Urge, push forward

4. Fourth planet from the Sun

( )

Male sheep

5. Free taster

( )

Daily servings of food

6. Italian herb

( )

Color between red and yellow

7. E.g. kettle, snare, or bass

( )

Wet earth

8. Houston's state

( )

Hatchets

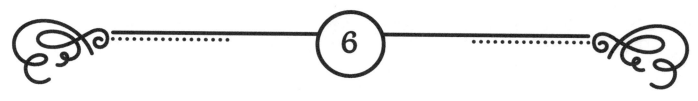

What links all five answers to these general knowledge quiz questions?

1. What bird is famous for laying its eggs in other birds' nests?

_____

2. What would be placed in a sconce, a torchère or a pricket?

_____

3. In the Old Testament, what relation was Abraham to Jacob?

_____

4. What kind of building has an apse, a narthex, and a steeple?

_____

5. What would a hydrophobe fear, and a hydrologist study?

_____

MISSING LINK:

_____

Can you unjumble these six classics of American literature?

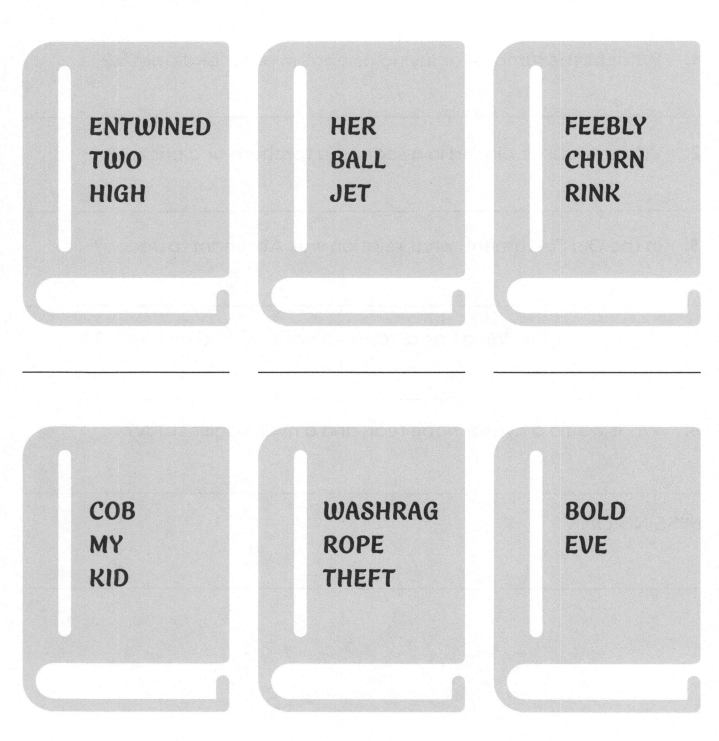

ENTWINED
TWO
HIGH

HER
BALL
JET

FEEBLY
CHURN
RINK

COB
MY
KID

WASHRAG
ROPE
THEFT

BOLD
EVE

Maybe it's time for a new hobby? Can you correctly match the word for the collector or enthusiast on the left with whatever it is that interests them on the right? The first answer has been filled in already to give you a head start...

1. Ornithologist	**A.** Stamps
2. Philatelist	**B.** Matchboxes
3. Cruciverbalist	**C.** Books
4. Phillumenist	**D.** Birds
5. Vexillologist	**E.** Coins
6. Oenophile	**F.** Archery
7. Bibliophile	**G.** Music
8. Numismatist	**H.** Wine
9. Toxophilite	**I.** Flags
10. Audiophile	**J.** Crosswords

How about a trip to the theater? Twelve of the answers in the boxes below are the names of famous playwrights and dramatists. The other 12 are the names of writers better known for their stories and poetry, not their plays! Cross out the names of all the poets and novelists, and then take the first letter of the remaining 12 playwrights' names in order—top to bottom, left to right—to spell out the name of a famous stage musical.

KEATS	IBSEN	NICHOLS	AUDEN
TERENCE	FROST	ORTON	TOLLER
DONNE	SHELLEY	HOUSMAN	EURIPIDES
CUMMINGS	WILLIAMS	PLATH	O'NEILL
ODETS	NERUDA	DIDEROT	STRINDBERG
HUGHES	YEATS	DICKINSON	WHITMAN

HIDDEN ANSWER:

_____

Complete the grid so that each line and column,
and each 9x9 square, contains the numbers 1–9.

	8		2				7	
7	4			1		8		
		1						
						6	2	
					6			
3				5		7		8
	1			8		9		
2	9				3		5	
	5					1		

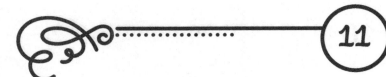 

Three 10-letter items from around the bedroom have been split up into five pairs of neighboring letters and jumbled up below. Can you correctly rejoin the pairs to rebuild the original words?

AL   AR   CA   CK   GH

LL   LO   MC   ND   NI

OW   PI   SE   TA   TS

_____

_____

_____

You've earned yourself a cup of tea!
Can you find your way through the maze to reach it?

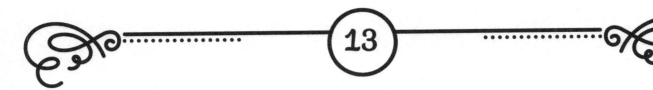
The answers to the clues on the right here contain **all but one** of the same letters as the clues on the left. Solve the clues, then write the unused letter in the middle circle to spell out—down the middle—a popular vacation destination. The first set has already been solved for you to give you an idea...

| 1. Paris' country | (F) | Tall water bird |
| FRANCE | | CRANE |

| 2. Remote wilds | ( ) | Peculiarity, strangeness |

| 3. Communal toilet, as in the army | ( ) | Family member |

| 4. Wriggle, squirm | ( ) | Color of the stars on the Stars and Stripes |

| 5. Pierce through on a spike | ( ) | Pancake syrup |

| 6. Synthetic or robotic human | ( ) | Invest into the church as a member of the clergy |

| 7. Maritime; sailor | ( ) | Coalworker |

Starting at the 5 in the top left corner of the grid, can you complete all the squares in this number puzzle, using each of the calculations to fill in the gaps? Some of the answers have already been filled in to give you a start.

5	x3		+10		√	
+3		-4		-9		+3
	+3	**11**	+5		+2	
x2		+9		+12		-1
	+4		+8	**28**	+4	
√		x2		+2		x3
4	x10		-10		-9	

Did you know that the average person spends anywhere from seven to nine hours every day sitting down? For people who work in an office, in fact, that figure is even higher: office workers spend three-quarters of their waking hours sat down during the working week! Now you've retired, of course, you've no excuse... How many of these seats and chairs can you find in the grid below?

```
K B S T O O L L A D D E R B A C K
E O U N T A H E E T T E S A D N E
A R T L W W E E O T U B F D I O N
R G O S C D I H H P U O Y E R T T
A S O C I L A N O I S A C C O U E
H N L Z K O L U G G F A Z K N F K
L A A I S I F O N B R G C C D I C
R R M Y P F N I V M A P D H A C U
O E B M E P W G C E I C C A C U B
S N E J O S E H C L S U K I K D L
D I R B D C A R U H O E A R R D W
N L G N I I K T S C A G A N J L I
I C E M R E G G C H A I R T G E S
W E R E G N U O L N U S R P S R N
G R E R I A H C L E V I W S L I R
```

ADIRONDACK ARMCHAIR BERGERE BUCKET CLUB COUCH CUDDLER
DECKCHAIR EGGCHAIR FUTON HAMMOCK LADDERBACK LAWSON LOVE SEAT
OCCASIONAL POUFFE RECLINER ROCKINGCHAIR SETTEE SLIPPER SOFA
STOOL SUNLOUNGER SWING SWIVELCHAIR TUB TULIP WINDSOR WINGBACK

What well known work–related phrase is
disguised as the rebus below?

WISE WORDS

"Retire from work, but not from life."
— MK Soni

Here's a tricky picture puzzle for you... How many six–sided hexagons are there in this grid of interlocking triangles?

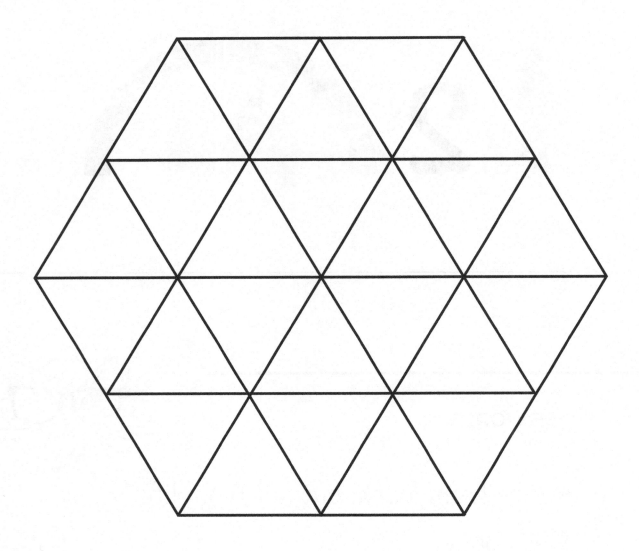

The letters in the names of two items of office equipment have been jumbled together here. What are they?

ACCEEEHILOOOOOPPRRRTTW

_____   _____

WISE WORDS

"The joy of retirement comes in those everyday pursuits that embrace the joy of life... and to allocate time to pursuits that only received, in years of working, a fleeting moment."
— Byron Pulsifer

Complete the grid so that each line and column,
and each 9x9 square, contains the numbers 1–9.

		2		6			3	
					4			
	6					8		
			8			3		1
				4			7	
	1		9		5			
5	3			7			6	
			1	8				
4		7						

"Oh no, it says here I've got a 9am meeting with a sun lounger."

What do you call a recently retired husband? Solve the quiz questions opposite and place the answers in the corresponding rows in the grid on the left to reveal the punchline reading down the shaded column…

#								
1.		N						
2.				S				
3.								Y
4.	I							
5.								L
6.								
7.		Y						N
8.			Z					
9.						F		
10.	M							
11.			G		R			
12.			A					
13.								T
14.			H					A
15.	A					A		
16.								O
17.			E					E
18.								A
19.			E					

1. What is the capital of Hawaii?
2. What is the surname of father and son pop singers Julio and Enriqué?
3. What day of the week is named after the sixth planet from the Sun?
4. Who (surname only) wrote the play *Cat On A Hot Tin Roof*?
5. How is the International Criminal Police Organization better known?
6. In what month is St. Valentine's Day?
7. What nationality was *Doctor Zhivago* star Omar Sharif?
8. In what Austrian city was Mozart born?
9. Who is the drunken lecherous knight in Shakespeare's *Merry Wives of Windsor*?
10. What 2007 Rihanna hit was No.1 on the Hot 100 for seven consecutive weeks?
11. What word for women's underwear comes from the French for linen?
12. What is the mainland part of the province of Newfoundland called?
13. What classic western features the character Rooster Cogburn? (4,4)
14. What body of water separates Britain and Ireland? (5,3)
15. Which Portuguese explorer (surname only) circumnavigated the world, 1519–22?
16. What is the name of the legendary lost South American city of gold? (2, 6)
17. What classic 1847 novel features the character Mr Rochester?
18. In what state are the cities of Stillwater, Enid, and Broken Arrow?
19. Which sporting legend's real first names were George Herman? (4,4)

How's your wine knowledge? If you're liable to now treat yourself to the odd glass or red or white of an evening, then here's the game for you. Match the wine type or region on the left with the country where it can be found on the right. The first answer has been filled in already to give you a head start...

1. Stellenbosch	**A.** Canada
2. Niagara	**B.** Chile
3. Pisco Atacama	**C.** France
4. Napa Valley	**D.** Italy
5. Beaujolais	**E.** Germany
6. Castile e León	**F.** South Africa
7. Mendoza	**G.** Spain
8. Chianti	**H.** USA
9. Rheingau	**I.** Mexico
10. Aguascalientes	**J.** Argentina

Twelve of the answers in the boxes below are songs recorded by the Beatles. The other 12 are all Rollings Stones tracks. Cross out the names of the Stones' songs, and then take the first letter of the remaining 12 Beatles' tracks in order—top to bottom, left to right—to spell out the name of one more Rolling Stones hit!

PAPERBACK WRITER	(I CAN'T GET NO) SATISFACTION	ALL MY LOVING	GET OFF OF MY CLOUD
SHE'S A RAINBOW	IN MY LIFE	NORWEGIAN WOOD	WILD HORSES
BROWN SUGAR	JUMPIN' JACK FLASH	TOMORROW NEVER KNOWS	SYMPATHY FOR THE DEVIL
I FEEL FINE	TUMBLING DICE	TAXMAN	BLACKBIRD
BEAST OF BURDEN	LET IT BE	YOU CAN'T ALWAYS GET WHAT YOU WANT	ALL YOU NEED IS LOVE
CAN'T BUY ME LOVE	ROCKS OFF	ANGIE	KANSAS CITY

HIDDEN ANSWER:

_____

ACROSS

1 Circumstances (7)

5 Additional (5)

8 Concur (5)

9 Outdated (8)

10 Austere; plain (5)

11 Unstructured (4,4)

14 In last position (8)

17 Perching bird (5)

19 Young frogs (8)

20 Relation by marriage (2–3)

21 Desert dweller (5)

22 Precisely (7)

DOWN

2 Should (5)

3 Belonging to them (6)

4 Wooden beam (6)

5 Give authority to (7)

6 Dinner jackets (7)

7 Outcome (9)

10 State of affairs (9)

12 Sports ground (7)

13 Forced oneself on (7)

15 From there (6)

16 Outdoor meal (6)

18 Creep (5)

What well known work–related phrase is disguised as the rebus below?

WISE WORDS

"You don't stop laughing when you grow old, you grow old when you stop laughing."
— George Bernard Shaw

All the answers to these clues can be made from the letters of the word LEISURE. Can you answer them all?

_____ **1.** Depends upon (6)

_____ **2.** Recycle (5)

_____ **3.** In __ of, instead or in place of (4)

_____ **4.** Certain (4)

_____ **5.** Irks, angers (5)

_____ **6.** Laws, directives (5)

_____ **7.** Snake–like fish (4)

_____ **8.** Entices (5)

_____ **9.** Hawaiian garlands (4)

_____ **10.** Spools of film (5)

Time to put your feet up in the sunshine!
Can you find your way through the maze to reach it?

The answers to the clues on the right here contain **all but one** of the same letters as the clues on the left. Solve the clues, then write this unused letter in the middle circle to spell out—down the middle—something you'll enjoy during your next vacation. The first set has already been solved for you to give you an idea...

1. Haphazard
RANDOM

(D) Ancient European empire
ROMAN

2. Spanish for "Spanish"!

Carpenter's tools

3. H2O

Rip

4. Microsoft search engine

Huge, gigantic

5. Dragged behind

Like an outstanding payment

6. E.g. O'Hare or Heathrow

Macaw

7. In the interim

Afternoon performance

8. Postponements

Unfortunately

Did you know that there's a word in Japanese, *tsundoku*, for the phenomenon of buying ever more books and just letting them pile up, unread, around your home? Now you're retired, of course, you've got no excuse...! How many of these favorite authors, past and present, can you find in the grid below?

```
M A R Q U E Z E T N O R B G G C K
Y S N E K C I D H E M I N G W A Y
L D I K Y O W R O W L I N G T B A
R L R Z N A R E R Y K P Y W R U T
E E E A N L U U T A R T O O S W J
G Z S W H U G O G C B O W T A R I
N V C A R R O L L I D N E I M P F
I E D K C O E L H O H N N K U S T
L R I D O S T O Y E V S K Y D I T
A N N K P R O U S T S A I J Y W E
S E T P L W R B S E M A J A A E L
R J R E V O O H N C O R N W E L L
M A R T I N T O L S T O Y Y E M O
Z T N O O K J D L A R E G Z T I F
C H R I S T I E G F G R I S H A M
```

ATWOOD   AUSTEN   BARRIE   BRONTE   BROWN
CARROLL   CHRISTIE   COELHO   CORNWELL   DAHL
DICKENS   DOSTOYEVSKY   DUMAS   FITZGERALD
FOLLETT   GRISHAM   HARDY   HEMINGWAY
HOOVER   HUGO   ISHIGURO   JAMES   JONES
KING   KOONTZ   LEWIS   MARQUEZ   MARTIN
ORWELL   PROUST   ROWLING   SALINGER
TOLKIEN   TOLSTOY   TWAIN   VERNE   WOOLF

Here's a word jumble to really get your brain ticking over...
On each line here, two answers have been mixed together
and their letters placed in alphabetical order between them.
Can you unjumble the two answers in each case? The first has
been solved for you to make a start!

BISHOP

QUEEN

1. Chess pieces
BEEHINOPQSU

2. Flightless birds
CEGHIINNOPRSTU

3. French cheeses
ABBCEEIMMRRT

4. South American capitals
AABDEEGIIJNOOOORRT

5. Ballroom dances
ADEFILLOOQRRTTUX

6. Roman emperors
AAACDDHIILNRSUU

Time for a road trip! The names of three 10–letter natural parks and landmarks from around the USA have been split up into five pairs of neighboring letters and jumbled up below. Can you correctly rejoin the pairs to rebuild the original words?

AC	AD	AT	BL	CR
ER	ER	ES	EV	GL
IL	KE	KH	LA	LS

_____

_____

_____

Complete the grid so that each line and column,
and each 9x9 square, contains the numbers 1–9.

		2	6			7	3	
5		6						
	9			3				
		9	2					
	5							
6	8		4	9	3			
				2	9	6		
					8		1	4
		3			6			5

How about an overseas vacation now you've all this spare time?
How many of these countries can you name from these closeups
of their national flags?

1. _____

2. _____

3. _____

4. _____

5. _____

6. _____

7. _____

8. _____

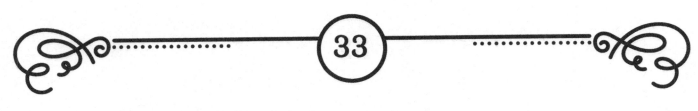

ACROSS

1 Edges of a piece of cloth (4)

3 Egyptian rulers (8)

9 Like an actor in an unsuitable role (7)

10 Protect (5)

11 What the adjective 'olfactory' relates to (5,2,5)

14 Container for ashes (3)

16 Set of twelve (5)

17 Title of a knight (3)

18 Science of wind resistance (12)

21 Ape (5)

22 Grand sailing ship (7)

23 Stern, diligent (8)

24 Unfortunately (4)

DOWN

1 Simple and plain (8)

2 Stoneworker (5)

4 Very warm (3)

5 In strict time or order (12)

6 Prophets, seers (7)

7 Carbonated pop (4)

8 Someone who listens in on a conversation (12)

12 Effervescent (5)

13 Gifts (8)

15 Requiring (7)

19 Perfect, most suitable (5)

20 Mark left by a wound (4)

22 Wildebeest (3)

Time for a movie night! Match the thriller on the left to its Hollywood star the right. The first answer has been filled in already to give you a head start...

1. Misery	**A.** Jodie Foster
2. The Hunt for Red October	**B.** Kathy Bates
3. Jaws	**C.** Sigourney Weaver
4. The Silence of the Lambs	**D.** Matt Damon
5. Jurassic Park	**E.** Meryl Streep
6. Alien	**F.** Al Pacino
7. The Talented Mr Ripley	**G.** Sean Connery
8. Dog Day Afternoon	**H.** Roy Scheider
9. Doubt	**I.** Sam Neill

If you're thinking of celebrating your retirement with a holiday or a world tour, here's a test of your geographical knowledge before you set off! Can you name the countries on this map of Europe?

1. _____ **2.** _____ **3.** _____ **4.** _____ **5.** _____

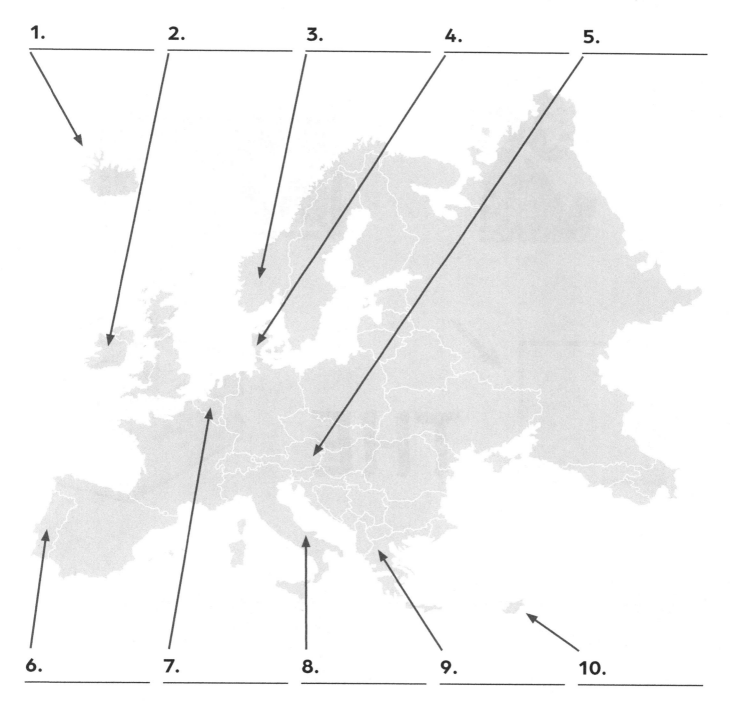

6. _____ **7.** _____ **8.** _____ **9.** _____ **10.** _____

What well known work–related phrase is disguised as the rebus below?

Complete the grid so that each line and column,
and each 9x9 square, contains the numbers 1–9.

5											2	7
					1							
2	4											
7												9
9						8	3					
					6		5				1	
	2	3										4
8	9					1	5					
					8						6	
						3						

It's five o'clock somewhere! So how about something a little stronger? How many of these cocktails and mixed liquors can you find in the grid below?

```
T  B  L  O  O  D  Y  M  A  R  Y  U  M  N  R  I  C
E  U  M  O  S  C  O  W  M  U  L  E  O  N  A  D  A
L  N  H  E  N  S  I  D  E  C  A  R  J  T  U  E  N
M  A  K  L  S  G  N  I  T  O  R  G  I  W  S  N  E
I  T  O  H  O  E  I  O  N  Z  N  A  T  P  N  O  R
G  T  G  R  U  F  N  S  Y  I  M  E  O  I  I  I  O
L  A  R  J  R  B  E  L  L  I  N  I  M  N  L  H  P
W  H  M  M  S  L  F  S  H  A  L  M  A  A  L  S  A
I  N  S  O  P  N  E  G  R  O  N  I  R  C  O  A  G
N  A  P  I  L  Z  O  M  B  I  E  D  T  O  C  F  N
Z  M  S  R  C  A  R  E  Z  A  S  Z  I  L  M  D  I
K  C  O  S  M  O  P  O  L  I  T  A  N  A  O  L  S
O  N  I  C  E  D  T  E  A  F  I  F  I  D  T  O  Z
D  A  I  Q  U  I  R  I  K  E  L  B  M  A  R  B  F
M  A  R  G  A  R  I  T  A  S  P  R  I  T  Z  E  R
```

BELLINI   BLOODY MARY   BRAMBLE   COSMOPOLITAN   DAIQUIRI
GIMLET   ICED TEA   LONG ISLAND   MAI TAI   MANHATTAN   MARGARITA
MARTINI   MOJITO   MOSCOW MULE   NEGRONI   OLD FASHIONED
PALOMA   PIÑA COLADA   PISCO   SAZERAC   SIDECAR   SINGAPORE
SLING   SOURS   SPRITZER   TOM COLLINS   ZOMBIE

Time for a matinée! Can you find your way through the maze to pick up the tickets on the other side?

The answers to the clues on the right here contain **all but one** of the same letters as the clues on the left. Solve the clues, then write this unused letter in the middle circle to spell out—reading down the middle—something you might enjoy during your next vacation. The first set has already been solved for you to give you an idea…

1. Phobia

(F)

FEAR

Organ of hearing

EAR

_____   _____

2. Red–breasted bird

( )

Innate, instinctive

_____   _____

3. Yacht clubs, sailing docks

( )

Pilot

_____   _____

4. *Tess of the d'Urbervilles* author Thomas

( )

Measure of 3ft

_____   _____

5. Sixth color of the rainbow

( )

Australian wild dog

_____   _____

6. Royal headwear

( )

Rockstar Sheryl

_____   _____

7. Boar, sow

( )

16th Greek letter

_____   _____

WORK

RETIREMENT

All the answers to these clues can be made from the letters in the word DOWNTIME. Can you answer them all?

1. Coarse cotton fabric (5)

2. Possessed (5)

3. Produced new coins (6)

4. Thick string (5)

5. Belonging to me; marine explosive (4)

6. Prong of a fork (4)

7. Salamander (4)

8. Central part of a city (7)

9. Rounded rooftop (4)

10. Of a lawn, cut (4)

11. Strengthened a muscle (5)

12. French for 'world' (5)

Starting at the 9 in the top left corner of the grid, can you complete all the squares in this number puzzle, using each of the calculations to fill in the gaps? Some of the answers have already been filled in to give you a start.

9	x 3	[ ]	+ 3	[ ]	÷ 10	**3**
+ 8		– 7		–16		+ 6
[ ]	+ 3	[ ]	– 6	[ ]	– 5	[ ]
– 2		–12		+10		√
[ ]	– 7	[ ]	x 3	**24**	÷ 8	[ ]
÷ 3		+2		– 3		+ 4
5	+ 5	[ ]	+ 11	[ ]	÷ 3	**7**

You know what makes retirement so great? You don't have to worry about... what? Fill the answers to these trivia questions into the corresponding rows in the grid on the right to reveal the punchline reading down the shaded column!

#						
1.						E
2.	D					
3.		A		U		
4.			A			
5.	E					
6.			V			
7.		M				
8.	P				E	
9.		I				
10.					A	
11.	E					
12.			A			

#						
13.				R		
14.						
15.			S			
16.						I
17.				I	T	
18.	S					D
19.			Z			
20.	I					N
21.	M					A
22.		W				
23.		O				

1. The Great Blue Hole is a tourist attraction off the coast of what Central American country?
2. What was the name of Henry VIII's only son?
3. In mythology, whose wax wings melted when he flew too close to the sun?
4. What native nation is the largest federally recognized tribe in the United States?
5. *Guten Tag* is a greeting in what language?
6. What name links Klein, Coolidge, and Harris?
7. What nut is used to make marzipan?
8. Who (surname only) wrote *Rabbit, Run*?
9. A dobro is a type of what musical instrument?
10. What is the capital of Cuba?
11. In what sport is a score of zero called "love"?
12. Who is Daisy Duck's boyfriend?
13. What is the oldest university in England?
14. In what ocean is Mauritius found?
15. Who (surname only) wrote the country music standard *Funny How Time Slips Away*?
16. What star sign covers June 1?
17. Who (surname only) was commander of the US Pacific Fleet during World War Two?
18. Who (surname only) shot and killed President John F Kennedy in 1963?
19. What classic character was created by the novelist Edgar Rice Burroughs?
20. What famous hotel chain was founded in Cisco, Texas, 1919?
21. What is the first name of *The Crown* and *Harry Potter* actress Staunton?
22. What is the largest city in New Jersey?
23. Who is the patron saint of England?

Time for a quick game? You shuffle, I'll deal!

```
F  M  E  D  L  O  H  S  A  X  E  T  T  P  R  Y  A
O  S  B  O  U  R  R  E  S  P  A  D  E  S  D  M  T
P  A  T  I  E  N  C  E  G  M  F  G  M  T  U  M  S
D  K  S  H  E  G  D  I  R  B  P  J  Y  R  P  U  A
N  V  I  N  G  T  E  T  U  N  I  B  S  A  P  R  N
A  O  H  P  D  I  M  S  G  D  Q  E  H  E  Y  Z  A
E  S  W  S  I  B  E  A  W  B  U  Z  I  H  R  B  C
T  G  N  F  A  N  L  Y  L  A  E  I  P  C  A  R  K
I  A  A  R  M  I  O  A  Z  I  T  Q  S  N  M  I  L
P  U  E  E  D  R  C  C  C  A  C  U  A  I  I  S  O
S  O  Y  E  L  O  I  Z  H  K  R  E  I  O  D  C  N
S  B  K  C  O  C  K  O  G  L  J  C  L  C  L  O  D
K  B  N  E  U  C  H  R  E  Z  E  A  S  O  M  L  I
A  M  Z  L  R  E  G  A  B  B  I  R  C  M  U  A  K
T  E  L  L  I  R  D  A  U  Q  T  K  N  K  A  S  E
```

BEZIQUE BLACKJACK BOURRE BRIDGE BRISCOLA CANASTA
CLOCK COINCHE CRAZY EIGHTS CRIBBAGE EUCHRE FREECELL
HEARTS KLONDIKE MALICE MY SHIP SAILS OLD MAID PATIENCE
PINOCHLE PIQUET POKER PYRAMID QUADRILLE RUMMY SKAT
SNAP SPADES SPITE AND TEXAS HOLD 'EM VINGT ET UN WHIST

Let's get some fresh air and take a trip to the great outdoors! Twelve of the answers in the boxes below are trees. The other 12 are flowers and grasses. Cross out the names of flowers, and then take the first letter of the remaining 12 answers in order—top to bottom, left to right—to spell out the name of one more type of tree.

NUTMEG	OAK	BAMBOO	REDWOOD
MARRAM	ESPARTO	WILLOW	CARNATION
THISTLE	ASPEN	YEW	SYCAMORE
AMARILLIS	PAMPAS	CITRONELLA	DARNEL
POPLAR	ROWAN	ANEMONE	UMBRELLA
GERANIUM	CONIFER	ALLIUM	ELM

HIDDEN ANSWER:

_____

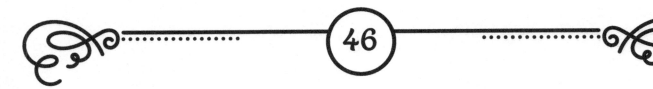

Time for a spot of bird watching! Three 10–letter birds' names have been split up into five pairs of neighboring letters and jumbled up below. Can you correctly rejoin the pairs to rebuild the original words?

AD   AD   ER   ER   FI

KI   LA   ME   NG   NN

OW   RK   RO   RU   SH

Complete the grid so that each line and column,
and each 9x9 square, contains the numbers 1–9.

		2			4			
					8	5		9
3	9	5					2	
			1					5
				8		4		
	8				5	6	1	
2						1		7
		3						
9		4		1				8

Here's a tricky test of general knowledge to get that gray matter working! Can you correctly match the description on the left to the relevant number on the right? The first answer has been filled in already to give you a head start...

1. Players in a quartet

2. Stars on the flag of Australia

3. Square root of 9

4. Sides in a nonagon

5. Moons of Mars

6. Cyclops' eyes

7. Bones in the human neck

8. Biblical Plagues of Egypt

9. Notes in an octave

10. V in Roman numerals

A. One

B. Two

C. Three

D. Four

E. Five

F. Six

G. Seven

H. Eight

I. Nine

J. Ten

RETIREMENT IS...

WEEKLY PLANNER

Sunday Monday Tuesday Wednesday Thursday Freeday Saturday

Whatever I want to do!

ACROSS

1 Flesh (4)

3 Happening often (8)

9 Tomato sauce (7)

10 Eject (5)

11 Incomparable, unparalleled (6,2,4)

13 Charge more than appropriate (3–3)

15 Large grapefruit–like citrus fruit (6)

17 Refilling a store (12)

20 Water bird (5)

21 Percussion instrument comprising a pair of hollow wooden shakers filled with dried beans (7)

22 Church vespers (8)

23 Upper limbs (4)

DOWN

1 Check (4,4)

2 Loft (5)

4 Renown, fame (6)

5 Wife of a reigning king (5,7)

6 Financial outgoing (7)

7 Relate a story (4)

8 Gratitude (12)

12 Blocks up (8)

14 Come before (7)

16 Spike on a sundial (6)

18 Become subject to (5)

19 Monstrous giant (4)

Complete the grid so that each line and column,
and each 9x9 square, contains the numbers 1–9.

	7	6		8				
			3				7	4
1				5				
	5				2		8	3
4			5		8			
3	9		7	4				
						8	3	
								1
	3						9	5

What well known work–related phrase is disguised as the rebus below?

 2  1

WISE WORDS

"Don't act your age in retirement.
Act like the young person you've always been!"
— JA West

Time to put your feet up! Can you find your way through the maze to take a seat on the couch on the other side?

The answers to the clues on the right here contain **all but one** of the same letters as the clues on the left. Solve the clues, then write this unused letter in the middle circle—reading down the middle—to spell out something you might have more time for now that you're retired. The first set has already been solved for you to give you an idea...

1. Apparition   (G)   Single gulp of liquor

GHOST   **SHOT**

2. Cabbage–like vegetable   ( )   Large deer

3. Item of clothing   ( )   Attracting metal

4. Heartbeat–raising exercise   ( )   Egyptian capital

5. Decreased, receded   ( )   Sunrise

6. Most populous country   ( )   Sesame–like edible seeds

7. Shorten a text or book   ( )   Animal that lives in a sett

8. Strait of water   ( )   French fashion house

9. Hard metamorphic rock   ( )   Interior surface of the eye

When Meryl Streep was once asked about retirement, she said
that she doesn't really tend to give it much thought.
"In our business," she said, "you're not kicked out necessarily…!"
How many movies starring one of Hollywood's greatest actors
can you find in the grid below?

```
E A G T D H F O S A G E C O U N T Y J
G O F O T M O I N T O T H E W O O D S
H F U U S E S B R N K S M U S I C O F
C B O M U L E B O B M A M M A M I A B
T I D U G T I Y M T S O P E H T S J B
H O T H U T R A E H E H T K M R F O X
E E K S A I E D H R E T N U H R E E D
I V J Z A L S H E A R T B U R N U Z E
R I N O I T A T P A D A R P S R A E W
O L L J R E N D I T I O N W O M E N S
N A O U T O F A F R I C A T W B C T I
L N R M F Y U N F O R T U N A T E I L
A G T H E D E V I L T H E H O U R S K
D E G A D L I W R E V I R E H T N C W
Y L E M O N Y S N I C K E T S H M U O
N S G R E C I O H C S E I H P O S U O
F W D O N T L O O K U P S T N E V E D
```

ADAPTATION

AUGUST / OSAGE COUNTY

DEER HUNTER   DON'T LOOK UP

DOUBT   EVIL ANGELS

FANTASTIC / MR FOX

HEARTBURN   INTO THE WOODS

LEMONY SNICKET'S / A SERIES OF /

UNFORTUNATE / EVENTS

LITTLE / WOMEN   MAMMA MIA

MUSIC OF / THE HEART

OUT OF AFRICA   RENDITION

SILKWOOD   SOPHIE'S CHOICE

THE DEVIL / WEARS PRADA

THE HOURS   THE IRON LADY

THE POST   THE RIVER WILD

Here's a tricky puzzle to get your head around... The answers to these questions fit letter by letter into the numbered boxes below. Move each numbered letter into its corresponding place in the coded passage below, and once all the boxes are filled in, a famous quip about retired life by Gene Perret will be spelled out. The first question has been answered and filled in already to make a start!

"
_____   ___ __ __ __ __   __ A K __ __ __   __ __
45   36 11 29 13 42   54 3 5 51 18 38   6 7

___ __ __   __ __ __   __ __ __ __ __ __   __ __
30 31 50   28 27 14   38 42 46 32 24 44   8 17

__ __   __ __   __ __ __ __   S __   __
19 43   33 15   10 26 48 49   1 23   37

__ __   __ __   H __ __ __   __ __
45 53   55 12   40 2 35 57   9 44

__ __ R __   __ __ __ __   __   __ __ . "
56 34 20 4   16 22 21 25   43   52 47 41

1. What kind of creature is a mako?

¹S	²H	³A	⁴R	⁵K

2. What word precedes Girl and Funk in the title of two US number 1 singles?

6	7	8	9	10	11

3. What is the name of Dorothy's dog in the *Wizard of Oz*?

12	13	14	15

4. What organ of the body is covered in cells called taste buds?

16	17	18	19	20	21

5. What is the seasonal rainy season in southeast Asia known as?

22	23	24	25	26	27	28

6. What word for a school caretaker derives from the name of Janus, the Roman god of entrances and gateways?

29	30	31	32	33	34	35

7. How many is there in four score?

36	37	38	39	40	41

8. What fictional bear has a friend called Boo-Boo?

42	43	44	45

9. What is usually the first animal listed in a dictionary?

42	43	44	45	46	47	48	49

10. Who was the legendary lover of Aeneas?

50	51	52	53

11. In the Bible, what relation was Abigail to Nabal?

54	55	56	57

Time for a well-earned break after that last puzzle!
Can you unjumble these mixed-up coffee orders?

1. COCA CUP PIN
   _____

2. BLANK CLOG
   _____

3. TALE T
   _____

4. SOS SPREE
   _____

5. CAT DOOR
   _____

6. CHOAM
   _____

7. CINEMA OAR
   _____

8. CHAOTIC MA
   _____

9. WHEAT LIFT
   _____

10. FACED
    _____

11. FAPPER
    _____

Here's another tricky word jumble to keep you busy!
On each line here, two answers have been mixed together
and their letters placed in alphabetical order between them.
Can you unjumble the two answers in each case? The first has
been solved for you to make a start.

CELLO

1. Stringed instruments
CEIILLLNOOV

VIOLIN

2. Three-dimensional shapes
BCCDEEILNRUY

3. Swimming strokes
ABCEFLLRRTTUWY

4. Asian islands
AAADHIJKKOOV

5. Punctuation marks
ACCEILMMMNOOOS

6. Culinary herbs
AEEGHMNOORTY

All the answers to these clues can be made from the letters in the word SUNBATHE. Can you answer them all?

_____

_____

_____

_____

_____

_____

_____

_____

_____

_____

1. Not present (6)

2. Hurries, increases speed (5)

3. Regular bar (5)

4. Flammable gas used as fuel (6)

5. Assists in a criminal matter (5)

6. Detests (5)

7. Sombrero, e.g. (6)

8. Ousts, removes from power (7)

9. Second Greek letter (4)

10. Italian volcano (4)

The names of three eight–letter car parts and features have been split up into five pairs of neighboring letters and jumbled up below. Can you correctly rejoin the pairs to rebuild the original words?

AT DI ER ET

IL OD OM OR

PE PI RA TA

_____

_____

_____

ACROSS

7 Turned into (6)

8 Named (6)

9 Unwanted plant (4)

10 Haste (8)

11 Newborn (7)

13 Oil spill (5)

16 Fabricator (5)

19 Makes smaller (7)

23 State of being somewhere (8)

24 Stage production (4)

25 Lie or roll in mud (6)

26 Producing flowers (6)

DOWN

1 Erase (6)

2 Enrage (6)

3 Removes confidential details from a document (7)

4 Large sea (5)

5 Flowery (6)

6 Madcap, very busy (6)

12 Tree that produces acorns (3)

14 Tavern (3)

15 Fastest land mammal (7)

17 Pilot (6)

18 Without difficulty (6)

20 Pierce through (6)

21 Loud horn or siren (6)

22 Blizzards, sleets (5)

Retirement is when you come home from work one day, and greet your other half with the words... what? Fill the answers to the quiz questions below in the corresponding rows in the grid on the right to find out the punchline!

#						
1.		L				
2.	S				P	
3.			C			
4.						
5.		B				V
6.	X					
7.				E		S
8.	R					
9.		S	S			
10.			B			

#						
11.		S		E		
12.						A
13.						
14.	R					
15.		I		R		
16.			H			
17.	L		C			A
18.		C				
19.			H			
20.			M			

1. What is the capital of Nova Scotia?
2. In physics, what is a molecule with the same atomic number as another but a different number of neutrons called?
3. Who (surname only) was the first signatory of the Declaration of Independence?
4. In what month is Halloween?
5. Who (surname only) wrote *Lolita*?
6. What is a volcano that will no longer erupt known as?
7. What MLB team were originally known as the Highlanders?
8. Ulster is a province of what European country?
9. What does the M in SMS stand for?
10. Who (surname only) won Best Actress Oscars in 1934, 1968, 1969, and 1982?
11. What marine mollusks produce pearls?
12. Whose hits include Vogue and Frozen?
13. What is the highest mountain in the world?
14. On TV, what are Rachel, Phoebe, Monica, Chandler, Joey, and Ross known as?
15. What is the 15th letter of the Greek alphabet?
16. Which English king was known as the Lionheart?
17. Who was the daughter of Agamemnon and Clytemnestra in Greek legend?
18. What word for an immunological injection comes from the Latin for 'cow'?
19. In 1928, who became the first woman to fly solo nonstop across the Atlantic?
20. In what 1988 movie did Tom Cruise and Dustin Hoffman play brothers? (4,3)

What do you call someone who's happy on a Monday morning?

RETIRED!

Retirement is the perfect time to take up a new sport... so long as you can find the time! Can you match the famous 21st–century sports stars on the left to their sports on the right? The first answer has been filled in already to give you a head start...

1. Novak Djokovic

2. Lionel Messi

3. Tom Watson

4. Kevin Durant

5. Lewis Hamilton

6. Manny Pacquiao

7. Maurice Greene

8. Ryan Murphy

9. Simone Biles

10. Katie Zaferes

A. Soccer

B. Golf

C. Boxing

D. Athletics

E. Triathlon

F. Tennis

G. Swimming

H. Gymnastics

I. Formula 1

J. Basketball

The answers to these five questions all have something in common. What is it?

1. What US city is home to the Sheldon Museum of Art and Pinnacle Bank Arena?
2. What does Tom Hanks name his volleyball friend in the movie *Cast Away*?
3. Which legendary king wielded a magical sword named Excalibur?
4. What cartoon cat is known for his love of lasagna and his hatred of Mondays?
5. What automobile company's models include the Escort and the Mustang?

HIDDEN ANSWER: _____

WISE WORDS

"Retirement, a time to do what you want to do, when you want to do it, where you want to do it and how you want to do it."

Complete the grid so that each line and column,
and each 9x9 square, contains the numbers 1—9.

			8	9		1		7
	5				6			
	4		2					3
		4	6	5	3			
2					9			
	1				8			
	7							
	6	8	5				4	
		5	4				7	8

Did you know that in 2019, a survey found that almost two-thirds of retired people over the age of 65 are keen gardeners? Whether you've a green thumb or not, have fun tracking down these (entirely genuine!) names for different types of orchids in the grid below!

```
P U T T Y R O O T A F L D R R I T D
E E N A E A S Y E S P A C E E D I K
R N H D K L T S L A S D C W B A G C
P U A N N U R S R M P Y P O B B E O
V N L A O C I A A T O S I L U T R R
A J L V M A P R C S T S L F T C S E
N A O E O T E G S I T L G Y T A M L
I L W U W C G T B R E I I A E T O B
L F E L L E D I E H D P B M R T U O
L W E B D P J G S C C P I O F L T N
A D N E N S B E R T A E T T L E H D
S P I D E R L R L P T R S H Y Y W Y
I R S A A K H O L Y G H O S T A O E
F B L A C K F I D D L E A S T E R V
P S H O W Y O Y R D E L F F U R W O
F A C E I E P Y D A L G N I C N A D
```

BIG-LIP   BLACK FIDDLE

BLUE VANDA   BUTTERFLY

CATTLEYA   CHRISTMAS

COCKLESHELL   DANCING LADY

DOVE   EASTER   FACE

FRIED-EGG   GRASS

HALLOWEEN   HOLY GHOST

JEWEL   LADY'S SLIPPER

MAYFLOWER   MONKEY

MOTH   NOBLE ROCK

NUN   PUTTY-ROOT

RUFFLED   SCARLET

SHOWY   SPECTACULAR

SPIDER   SPOTTED CAT

STRIPE   TIGER

TIGER'S MOUTH   VANILLA

The answers to the clues on the right here contain **all but one** of the same letters as the clues on the left. Solve the clues, then write this unused letter in the middle circle to spell out—reading down the middle—something you won't need now that you're retired. The first set has already been solved for you to give you an idea...

1. Upper leg

THIGH _____

(T)

Lofty

HIGH

2. Round red salad vegetable

_____

( )

Sliver, splinter

_____

3. Free taster

_____

( )

Legal appeals or claims

_____

4. Christian spring festival

_____

( )

Ogle, gawp at

_____

5. Caskets, boxes

_____

( )

Two-player game of strategy

_____

6. Cluelessly inexperienced

_____

( )

Long trailing plant tendril

_____

7. Grooms' partners

_____

( )

Removes moisture

_____

8. Regional, nearby

_____

( )

Fossil fuel

_____

9. Bumpkins

_____

( )

Yellows of eggs

_____

We're back down the library!
Can you unjumble these six more classics of American literature?

HOT
FREEMAN

THY
GARBAGE
TEST

EASED
OFTEN

A
NEW
FIGHT

HARDEN
TOO

CHORTLE
PUP
ROLE

What phrase from the world of work is encoded in the rebus below?

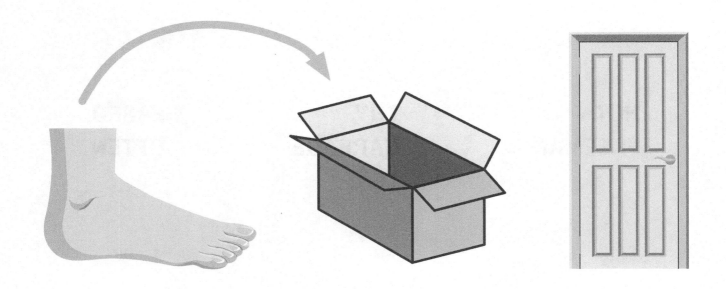

Let's plan another overseas adventure! Can you name the numbered countries in South America from their location on the map below?

1. _____
_____

2. _____
_____

3. _____
_____

4. _____
_____

5. _____
_____

6. _____
_____

7. _____
_____

8. _____
_____

Can you find your way through the maze to take
a hike in the hills on the other side?

If you're looking for a new hobby in your retirement, how about something culinary? Twelve of the answers in the boxes below are soups, stews, and broths. The other 12 are types of bread. Cross out the breads, and then take the first letter of the remaining 12 soups in order—top to bottom, left to right—to spell out the name of one more type of bread.

BAGUETTE	CIABATTA	POZOLE	UKHA
COB	MINESTRONE	PHO	ESCUDELLA
SPELT	RAMEN	BLOOMER	FARMHOUSE
NAVARIN	NAAN	IRISH	PANINI
COQ AU VIN	KARE-KARE	SODA	ROTI
ÉTOUFFÉE	BRIOCHE	LANCASHIRE HOTPOT	STOTTIE

HIDDEN ANSWER:

_____

Starting at the 7 in the top left corner of the grid, can you complete all the squares in this number puzzle, using each of the calculations to fill in the gaps? Some of the answers have already been filled in to give you a start.

7	x 2		+ 6		÷ 4	**5**
+ 5		+ 6		+ 1		+ 2
	+ 8	**20**	+ 1		÷ 3	
x 3		÷ 5		– 13		+ 9
	÷ 9		x 2		x 2	**16**
+ 4		+ 6		x 4		÷ 4
	÷ 4		+ 22		÷ 8	

Just because you've put your feet up doesn't mean you can't get out and about! Hidden in this grid are 29 of the places, activities, and other things you might go to or get up to on a city break or a weekend away!

```
P A E G C T R O P R I A K M A O Y
A K F N T F O R E S T A U R A N T
L B A I U I K Z A Y B S T O B M N
A O C P O J J F U T E G S T G O S
C A T P G U A T S U A N T E N U S
E T H O N R D A M L C D H K I N T
O T E H I G F W L E H N C R H T R
H O A S T K N E S E W A A A T A E
O U T D A A R I K G J D Y M A I E
T R E E E Y U I M E I E I A B N T
E H R R P R H I Y M Z B U E N T F
L B I L C O C K T A I L S L U R O
G N I L L E K R O N S W A F S A O
N A T I O N A L P A R K S Z J I D
G A R D E N R N A N I R A M J L I
```

AIRPORT   ART GALLERY   BEACH   BED AND   BREAKFAST   BOAT TOUR
CAFE   COCKTAILS   CRUISE   EATING OUT   FLEA MARKET   FOREST
GARDEN   HIKE   HOTEL   MARINA   MOUNTAIN TRAIL   MUSEUM   NATIONAL
PARK   PALACE   RESTAURANT   SAFARI   SHOPPING   SNORKELLING
STREET FOOD   SUNBATHING   SWIMMING   THEATER   YACHT

ACROSS

1	Laugh slightly (7)
5	Insignificant (5)
8	Cerebral organ (5)
9	Ingenious devices (7)
10	Boring a hole (8)
11	Marine mammal (4)
13	Battle (6)
14	Not capable (6)
17	Porridge grains (4)
19	Wrist adornment (8)
22	Enthusiastically (7)
23	Discover (5)
24	Name (5)
25	Repels (7)

DOWN

1	Multiplied threefold (5)
2	Radioactive element (7)
3	Shakespeare tragedy (4,4)
4	Motor (6)
5	Produced (4)
6	Daughter of a sibling (5)
7	Settle a problem (7)
12	Finger joints (8)
13	Most nearby (7)
15	Love songs (7)
16	Godly entreaty (6)
18	Restrictive, narrow (5)
20	Musical notes (5)
21	Without cost (4)

WISE WORDS

"When a man retires, the wife gets twice the husband but half the income."
— Chi Chi Rodriguez

Three 8–letter words from the world of technology have been split up into four pairs of neighboring letters, and jumbled up below. Can you correctly rejoin the pairs to rebuild the original words?

CO   ER   KE   LE

MP   OA   RD   RE

SS   UT   WI   YB

_____

_____

_____

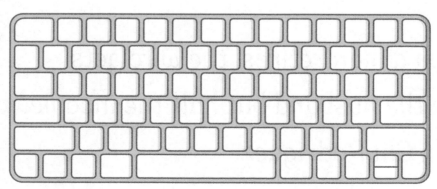

All the answers to these clues can be made from the letters in the word GARDENING. Can you answer them all?

_____ **1.** Male goose (6)

_____ **2.** Angering (8)

_____ **3.** Small blade or stabbing sword (6)

_____ **4.** Making money (7)

_____ **5.** The Never-__ Story (6)

_____ **6.** Warming spice (6)

_____ **7.** Scoring test papers (7)

_____ **8.** Smiled widely (7)

_____ **9.** Rio ___, the longest river in Mexico (4)

_____ **10.** Peril (6)

How is your wordpower? Can you correctly match each of the more obscure words on the left to their more familiar synonyms on the right? The first answer has been filled in already to give you a head start...

1. Heretofore

2. Acrimony

3. Capricious

4. Zephyr

5. Verisimilitude

6. Draconian

7. Pulchritudinous

8. Sagacious

9. Selcouth

10. Predilection

A. Unpredictable

B. Ruthless

C. Beautiful

D. Fondness

E. Previously

F. Bizarre

G. Truth

H. Breeze

I. Wise

J. Spite

Here's another tricky word jumble to keep you busy!
On each line here, two answers have been mixed together
and their letters placed in alphabetical order between them.
Can you unjumble the two answers in each case? The first has
been solved for you to make a start.

DRAGON
_____

MERMAID
_____

1. Mythical creatures
AADDEGIMMNORR

2. Camping equipment
ABEEGGILNNPSTT

_____   _____

3. Root vegetables
AINOOPPRTTTU

_____   _____

4. European seas
AAAADEEEEGIMNNNRRT

_____   _____

5. Baseball terms
ADDEIIKMNORST

_____   _____

6. Robert de Niro movies
AACDEIIINORRSTVX

_____   _____

The answers to the clues on the right here contain **all but one** of the same letters as the clues on the left. Solve the clues, then write this unused letter in the middle circle to spell out—reading down the middle—something you might like to learn a new one of now that you're retired. The first set has already been solved for you to give you an idea...

1. Fourth month	(L)	Set of two
APRIL		PAIR

| 2. Counting frame | ( ) | Aqualung diving |

| 3. *Birthday Party* playwright | ( ) | Shallow laboratory dish |

| 4. Moroccan city | ( ) | Keep hold of, preserve |

| 5. Performing as a duo | ( ) | Slightly discolored |

| 6. Despising, detesting | ( ) | Addams Family's hand |

| 7. Band, bunch of people | ( ) | Scold, pester |

| 8. *Frasier* actor, David Hyde | ( ) | Cost |

Do you know what a "sea-widow" is? It's a wife whose husband retires, buys a boat, and spends so much time looking after it that he might as well not be around any more! Try not to get quite so obsessed with this puzzle of sailboat parts and terms!

```
B P T R F B O O M P W B Y F A W R
A U I D U W I N C H U O F W C N D
C H P Y H D I E T R U U B O G O R
K M L T S R D P G S L L M R N I A
S D U E A P S E O U T P L P I H O
T R P H C E L R R A R O Y P C B
A A C O C K P I T N T S A T P N R
Y O O Y A T S N I A M T A P O A A
G B N N K D B O L C S C E S T T T
N R Y E Y J N E D E K L S K A S S
I E D C G W E T R A N S O M M I A
M T T R A K H O K G R M A S T Y L
A N J Y L I F E L I N E T T A B T
O E I S T E R N E D E C K J T M T
C C B B I N N A C L E D U O R H S
```

BACKSTAY BATTEN BINNACLE BOOM BOW BURGEE CENTERBOARD
COAMING COCKPIT COMPANIONWAY DECK FORESTAY GENOA HULL JIB
KEEL LEECH LIFELINE LUFF MAINSTAY MAST PORT PROW PULPIT
RUDDER SAIL SHROUD STANCHION STARBOARD STERN STRAP TACK
TOPPING TRANSOM WHEEL WINCH

Complete the grid so that each line and column,
and each 9x9 square, contains the numbers 1—9.

4			6		7	3		
					9	6	2	
				2				9
		2		3			9	
9			1					5
	5	8		9				
	4					5		7
					5	1		
							6	8

In this pyramid, each answer contains all the letters of the previous word plus one new letter. Can you fill all the gaps around the key word RETIRE to complete it?

E

1. Second note of the musical scale

2. Anger, wrath

3. Exhaust

4. One who attempts

5. Finish a lifetime of work — R E T I R E

6. Draft a text a second time

7. More diluted

8. Strong, illicit liquor

Retirement isn't the end of the road, someone wise once said—it's the beginning... what? Fill in the answers to the quiz questions below in the grid on the right to find the end of the quotation reading down the shaded column.

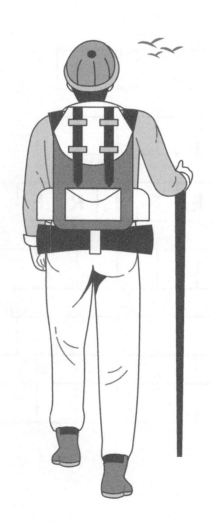

#						
1.	E					
2.	L					
3.				E		
4.	A					
5.						R
6.			S			
7.		U				G
8.	Z					
9.		N		V		
10.						E
11.		H				P
12.					Y	
13.	A				A	
14.		L				
15.						A
16.				S		

1. Which legendary Theban king unwittingly killed his father and married his mother?

2. What is the only US state on both the Gulf of Mexico and the Atlantic Ocean?

3. Who (surname only) wrote *Walden*?

4. What is the USA's oldest university?

5. What South American country is named for its geographical latitude?

6. What scientific principle states that electric current is directly proportional to voltage, and inversely proportional to resistance? (4,3)

7. What is the surname of the US chemist Linus, one of only two people to have won Nobel Prizes in two different fields?

8. Which Hebrew prophet was exiled to Babylon in 587 BCE?

9. What ancient city of Upper Mesopotamia was once the capital of the Assyrian Empire, and for a time in the 7th century BCE the largest city in the world?

10. What Beatles hit features the line "Take a sad song and make it better"? (3,4)

11. What is the name of the resurrected mummy in the 1999 horror *The Mummy*?

12. Which legendary filmmaker's surname puts the G in MGM Studios?

13. Which Roman emperor built a wall across northern England?

14. What first name is shared by the Dr Who actor Hartnell, the Scottish folk hero Wallace, *Lord of the Flies* author Golding, and British abolitionist Wilberforce?

15. What Caribbean island forms a sovereign nation with the island of Barbuda?

16. Who (surname only) was president of the Russian Federation from 1991–99?

ACROSS

1 Told in advance (10)

7 Castrated male chicken (5)

8 Result (7)

9 Miss out (4)

10 Late winter month (8)

12 Annually (6)

14 Greek L (6)

18 Cutting tool (8)

19 One of two equal parts (4)

21 Act of using money or gifts to sway someone's opinion (7)

22 Word of greeting (5)

23 Caustic, harsh (10)

DOWN

1 Place of manufacture (7)

2 Exact copy (7)

3 Sauvignon Blanc, e.g. (4)

4 Mediterranean island (6)

5 Outside (8)

6 Looked up to (7)

11 Sparkles (8)

13 Extract (7)

15 Writing system for the blind (7)

16 Offend (7)

17 Bleaker, duller (6)

20 Slender (4)

How many squares are there in total in this shape?

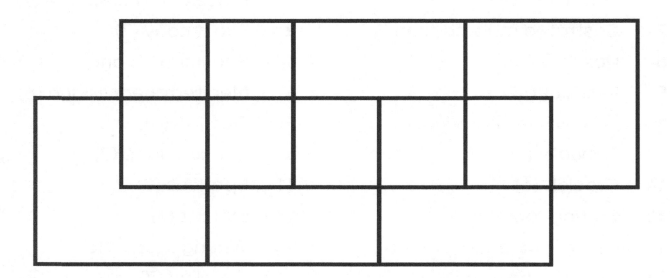

Time to take the dog for a walk! Can you find your way through the maze to grab the leash on the other side?

Complete the grid so that each line and column,
and each 9x9 square, contains the numbers 1–9.

	2		8	4	6			
	6				9		2	5
				3				
		6	4				5	
2		9				8		1
						6		
	8		3				6	
								9
		4	6		1	7		

Passports at the ready... The names of three 10–letter countries from around the world have been split up into five pairs of neighboring letters and jumbled up below. Can you correctly rejoin the pairs to rebuild the original words?

(AD)   (EA)   (EL)   (LA)   (LU)

(LV)   (MB)   (NE)   (ND)   (OR)

(OU)   (RG)   (SA)   (WZ)   (XE)

_____

_____

_____

ACROSS

1 Stretchy fabric
6 Artist's drawing tool
7 Household animal
8 Tires
11 Witch's incantations
12 Finish
14 Young cat
15 Firing mechanism

DOWN

2 Of greater length
3 Drops liquid
4 Bottle lid
5 Cowboy hat
6 Fueled, energized
9 Season of regrowth
10 Carefree
13 Stain, spot of color

Did you know that one of the best ways to keep your brain ticking over after retirement is to pick up a musical instrument? You might not quite thinking of taking on the bagpipes or the xylophone any time soon, but see if you can find them and all the other orchestra's-worth of instruments listed here in the grid below!

```
C O N C E R T I N A B R C E L L O
H P A N P I P E S B A O D W S R S
R I O H C T L T U T A O N T U B A
H A U D I C E A I T U S E G T L A
S N V Y J P C U L B B E S E O H G
T O K I M M G H L O L A N O Z S S
I L P U O F T E A P I I N T O I M
M S R R L L B O A R R V R J A N U
P T G U A A I N T A M O Y L O H R
A A T O S H S N L E M O G J C S D
N E B S O T J C F B R N N Z W T O
I W P I C C O L O B A G P I P E S
S A X O P H O N E R R U M J U H W
G N S Z G H E N O H P O L Y X M G
H A R M O N I C A C C O R D I O N
```

ACCORDION BAGPIPES BANJO BASSOON BONGOS CELLO CHOIR CLARINET CONCERTINA COR ANGLAIS DOUBLE BASS DRUMS FLUTE GUITAR HARMONICA HARMONIUM HARP ORGAN PANPIPES PIANO PICCOLO SAXOPHONE STEEL PANS TIMPANI TROMBONE TRUMPET TUBA VIOLA VIOLIN XYLOPHONE

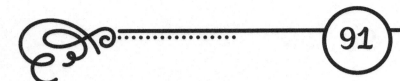
Let's head down the antiques market! Can you match the item on the left with its correct description from the right? The first answer has been filled in to give you a head start...

1. Armoire	**A.** Plant pot
2. Jardinière	**B.** Armchair
3. Canapé	**C.** Side table
4. Console	**D.** Wardrobe
5. Torchère	**E.** Sofa
6. Bureau	**F.** Chest of drawers
7. Caquetoire	**G.** Sideboard
8. Tallboy	**H.** Candlestick
9. Credenza	**I.** Bed
10. Four poster	**J.** Writing desk

Let's head to the east for our next vacation! Can you name all the countries of Asia numbered on this map?

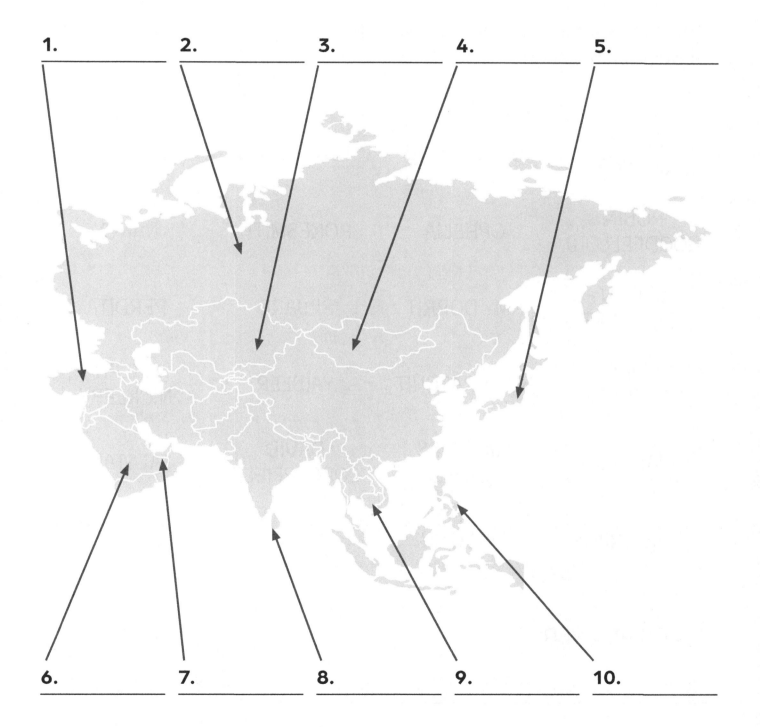

1. _____

2. _____

3. _____

4. _____

5. _____

6. _____

7. _____

8. _____

9. _____

10. _____

Twelve of the answers in the boxes below are the names of characters created by Charles Dickens. The other 12 are among Shakespeare's many characters. Cross out the Shakespearean names, then take the first letter of the remaining 12 Dickensian answers in order—top to bottom, left to right—to spell out the name of one of Dickens' novels.

PETER QUINCE	BROWNLOW	TOBY BELCH	ARTFUL DODGER
ROBIN GOODFELLOW	OPHELIA	ROKESMITH	NANCY
QUEEN MARGARET	AMY DORRIT	SIWARD	PERDITA
FRIAR LAURENCE	BOB CRATCHIT	YAWLER	RALPH NICKLEBY
URIAH HEEP	MISTRESS QUICKLY	DAVID COPPERFIELD	FALSTAFF
GRADGRIND	LAVATCH	BOTTOM	EBENEZER SCROOGE

HIDDEN ANSWER:

_____

The answers to the clues on the right here contain **all but one** of the same letters as the clues on the left. Solve the clues, then write this unused letter in the middle circle to spell out—down the middle—something that you might like to join now that you're retired. The first set has already been solved for you to give you an idea...

1. Pre-midday meal

BRUNCH

(B)

Swill milk to make butter

CHURN

2. 0° latitude

Un, deux, trois, ___

3. Excuses, explanations

Rope traps

4. Turning over a fire

Gold bars

5. Tar

White lining of a fruit skin

6. Baking staple

Players in a quartet

7. Tidal wave

Praying insect

8. Chest bones

Title of an English knight

Starting at the 10 in the top left corner of the grid, can you complete all the squares in this number puzzle, using each of the calculations to fill in the gaps? Some of the answers have already been filled in to give you a start.

10	÷ 2		+ 7		x 2	24
−4		x 3		+ 4		÷ 6
	+ 9	15	+ 1		√	
−2		+ 5		+12		x 6
4	x 5		+ 8		− 4	
x 2		+ 4		−7		−17
	x 3		−3		÷ 3	

"Now that I'm retired, I know exactly when it's time for bed. Two hours after I fall asleep on the couch."

All the answers to these clues can be made from the letters in the word RELAXATION. Can you answer them all?

1. Movable panel of an aircraft's wing (6)

2. Rich, dark beef soup (6)

3. Maker of men's clothing (6)

4. Vitamin A (7)

5. Dawdle, hang around (6)

6. Unreactive (5)

7. Embellished, overly decorated (6)

8. Justification, sound basis (9)

9. Largest bodily artery (5)

10. Extreme happiness (7)

In this crossword, all the answers are anagrams of the clues. If there's more than one possibility, you'll have to make sure you pick the right one!

ACROSS

1. NAMED **4.** ACRE **6.** PLATE **7.** RITE **8.** PICOSECOND
13. KISS **15.** LOGIN **16.** TIDE **17.** IDOLS

DOWN

1. AMPLE **2.** TONED **3.** DEALS **4.** ART **5.** ORGIC **9.** KNEAD
10. CLAMS **11.** PLANE **12.** COULD **14.** ITS

ACROSS

4 Ghosts (6)

8 Flair (7)

9 Glass front of a television (6)

10 Trains (7)

11 Arch of the foot (6)

12 Featuring, entailing (9)

14 Aubergines (9)

17 Sirens (6)

18 At an unspecified moment (7)

19 Ocean between Africa and Asia (6)

20 Abashed, sheepish (7)

21 Touch gently, pat (6)

DOWN

1 Tropical pool (6)

2 Package (6)

3 Collies (9)

5 Striding, walking back and forth (6)

6 Tip over (8)

7 Summary (8)

11 Incompetence (9)

12 Dwells in (8)

13 Kitchen strainer (8)

14 Set off on a trip (6)

15 Relating to the stars (6)

16 Interfere, meddle (6)

WISE WORDS

"It's nice to get out of the rat race. But you have to learn to get along with less cheese." — Gene Perret

Time to put our feet up for a reading break. Can you find your way through the maze to the books on the other side?

How's your green thumb? The names of three 10–letter plants and flowers have been split up into five pairs of neighboring letters and jumbled up below. Can you correctly rejoin the pairs to rebuild the original words?

AG   AP   DE   DR   HE

HI   LI   LP   NI   ON

OT   PE   RO   SN   UM

_____

_____

_____

Complete the grid so that each line and column,
and each 9x9 square, contains the numbers 1–9.

	3				1			
5			4		7	2	9	
				3				4
	7		3			9		
		1						8
		9	8		5			
		5				6		
	4		1	8			2	
		2	5		3			

Grab the popcorn and put your feet up in front of movie. Can you correctly match the Hollywood legend on the left with the movie in which they starred on the right? The first answer has been filled in already to give you a head start...

1. Gregory Peck	**A.** Sabrina
2. Paul Newman	**B.** To Kill A Mockingbird
3. Richard Burton	**C.** Barefoot in the Park
4. Audrey Hepburn	**D.** Cactus Flower
5. Barbra Streisand	**E.** Cat Ballou
6. Robert Redford	**F.** Cool Hand Luke
7. Goldie Hawn	**G.** All About Eve
8. Jane Fonda	**H.** The Quiet Man
9. John Wayne	**I.** Funny Girl
10. Bette Davis	**J.** Cleopatra

Here's something you might have on your retirement bucket list: writing a book! If you've been leaving writing your debut novel until you have more time, you'd not be alone: Raymond Chandler didn't publish *The Big Sleep* until he was 51, and Laura Ingalls Wilder didn't come up with her popular *Little House on the Prairie* stories until she was 65! How many of these literary terms can you find in the grid below?

```
N  D  D  A  E  L  C  I  T  N  A  M  O  R  L  F  M
O  D  S  T  K  T  S  I  N  O  G  A  T  O  R  P  P
I  C  T  I  I  O  T  R  C  H  A  R  A  C  T  E  R
S  H  O  N  T  L  F  O  T  E  N  D  I  N  G  U  O
U  A  R  N  N  P  C  T  K  R  J  W  N  A  M  E  S
L  P  Y  U  O  B  I  A  C  P  A  R  A  B  L  E  E
C  T  L  D  I  U  P  R  L  E  G  E  N  D  G  F  D
N  E  I  O  T  S  E  R  E  T  N  I  E  V  O  L  J
O  R  N  H  C  W  C  A  N  T  A  G  O  N  I  S  T
C  J  E  W  I  O  C  N  M  L  P  R  E  F  A  C  E
O  R  E  H  F  O  F  O  L  K  L  O  R  E  K  E  T
M  O  R  A  L  A  B  I  O  G  R  A  P  H  Y  B  W
T  L  J  O  B  G  V  P  A  R  A  G  R  A  P  H  I
F  A  L  L  E  V  O  N  Z  K  C  I  K  E  D  I  S
T  S  E  F  A  I  R  Y  T  A  L  E  Z  I  Z  K  T
```

ANTAGONIST   BIOGRAPHY   CHAPTER   CHARACTER
CONCLUSION   ENDING   EPIC   FABLE   FAIRYTALE
FICTION   FOLKLORE   HERO   LEGEND   LOVE INTEREST
MORAL   NAMES   NARRATOR   NOVELLA   PARABLE
PARAGRAPH   PREFACE   PROSE   PROTAGONIST
ROMANTIC LEAD   SIDEKICK   STORYLINE   SUBPLOT
TWIST   VILLAIN   WHODUNNIT

The only problem with retirement is that ... what? Fill in the answers to these quiz questions into the corresponding rows in the grid to discover the punchline reading down the shaded column!

#				
1.	E			
2.				E
3.				E
4.				
5.		Y		
6.		R		
7.	L			
8.				L
9.				A
10.		V		
11.	H			
12.				N
13.				A
14.		B		
15.	E			S
16.	R			
				D
			E	

1. What is the rising agent in a loaf of bread?
2. What unit of weight is equal to 1/16th of a pound?
3. According to some biblical accounts, what relation was Clopas to Jesus Christ?
4. What is the only direction it is possible to travel from the South Pole?
5. In what country does the river Nile reach the sea?
6. What is the surname of the French author Jules, whose works include *20,000 Leagues Under the Seas* and *Around the World in Eighty Days*?
7. What TV talk show ran for more than 3,200 episodes from 2003–2022?
8. In the United Kingdom, what word can precede Mail, Mint, Ballet, Academy, and Family?
9. In what Italian city was Christopher Columbus born?
10. Who did Austin Butler portray in a 2022 biopic?
11. Complete this sentence: THIS is to THAT as THESE is to ___ ?
12. Which US baseball star (surname only) was known by the nickname Hammerin' Hank?
13. What Greek letter shares its name with the mouth of a river?
14. What word for a collection of songs or photographs comes from the Latin for 'white'?
15. Which Irish writer penned the famous poem, *The Lake Isle of Innisfree*?
16. Which constellation has a famous 'belt' comprising the three stars Alnitak, Alnilam, and Mintaka?
17. Who (surname only) is credited as being the Father of Psychoanalysis?
18. What is the common name for the medical symptom pyrexia?

ACROSS

1 Double-cross (6)
4 Schoolwork (5)
9 Boldness, swagger (7)
10 Nightclub (5)
11 Thespian (5)
12 Someone easily upset or moved to tears (7)
13 Taking apart (11)
18 Wine merchant (7)
20 Poorest quality (5)
22 The Earth (5)
23 Sightseer (7)
24 Posed a question (5)
25 Foul smell (6)

DOWN

1 North American cat (6)
2 Expanse of land (5)
3 Word jumble (7)
5 On this date (5)
6 Contempt (7)
7 Pay close attention (11)
8 Asian capital (5)
14 Viscera (7)
15 Legal proceeding (7)
16 Promises (5)
17 Sew (6)
19 Bump, knock slightly (5)
21 Rule as monarch (5)

WISE WORDS

"The trouble with retirement is that you never get a day off." — Abe Lemons

One bad thing about retirement—now you've got no excuse not to tackle all of those odd jobs around the house you've been putting off for years…! So how about a little home improvement?

```
N  H  N  H  G  L  O  O  P  G  N  I  M  M  I  W  S
E  W  F  C  U  Z  I  S  N  E  T  A  R  O  C  E  D
H  R  I  R  N  Z  Z  Z  D  E  R  I  W  E  R  N  J
C  A  T  O  S  I  S  N  O  I  T  A  V  O  N  E  R
T  P  L  P  E  C  E  S  A  C  R  I  A  T  S  U  E
I  B  E  L  B  A  T  L  O  O  P  F  I  F  M  E  C
K  A  U  T  W  G  N  I  P  A  C  S  D  N  A  L  A
D  T  D  Z  E  A  W  A  L  L  P  A  P  E  R  B  P
G  H  R  G  D  J  Y  C  A  R  P  E  T  S  K  U  S
A  R  I  N  O  I  S  R  E  V  N  O  C  T  F  O  L
R  O  V  T  R  E  E  H  O  U  S  E  I  P  G  D  W
A  O  E  X  T  E  N  S  I  O  N  P  A  T  I  O  A
G  M  W  Y  R  O  T  A  V  R  E  S  N  O  C  K  R
E  G  A  M  E  S  R  O  O  M  O  O  R  N  U  S  C
P  L  Y  G  L  A  Z  I  N  G  R  E  P  A  I  N  T
```

BATHROOM   CARPETS   CONSERVATORY   CRAWLSPACE   DECORATE   DEN
DOUBLE   DRIVEWAY   EXTENSION   GAMES ROOM   GARAGE   GLAZING
HALLWAY   KITCHEN   LANDSCAPING   LOFT CONVERSION   PATIO   POOL TABLE
PORCH   RENOVATIONS   REPAINT   REWIRE   SNUG   STAIRCASE   SUNROOM
SWIMMING POOL   TREEHOUSE   WALLPAPER

Twelve of the answers in the boxes below are children's animated movies. The other 12 are live action kids' movies. Cross out the names of live action films, then take the first letter of the 12 remaining animated movies in order—top to bottom, left to right—to spell out the name of a 1993 blockbuster.

JUNGLE BOOK	FREAKY FRIDAY	MATILDA	UP
THE PARENT TRAP	MADELINE	RATATOUILLE	ALADDIN
FREE WILLY	HOMEWARD BOUND	SLEEPING BEAUTY	SWORD IN THE STONE
INSIDE OUT	CINDERELLA	POCAHONTAS	BABE
BEETHOVEN	THE WIZARD OF OZ	FLUBBER	THE LOVE BUG
ARISTOCATS	RESCUERS	GOONIES	KUNG FU PANDA

HIDDEN ANSWER:

_____

Time to try cracking another code... The answers to these quiz questions fit, letter by letter, into the numbered boxes below each one. Then, move each numbered letter into its corresponding space in the coded passage on the opposite page. Once all the boxes are filled in, it will spell out why the writer Jonathan Clements believes retirement is a lot like a long weekend in Vegas... The first question has been answered and filled in for you to make a start.

"

___ ___ ___   ___ ___ ___ ___   ___ ___   ___ ___
 9   17   34   44   14   22   2   57   6   38   24

___ ___ ___ ___ ___   ___ ___   ___ ___   ___ ___ ___
18   50   12   32   35   59   25   4   27   40   39   11

___ ___ ___ ___ ___ ___ ___ '   ___ ___ ___   ___ ___ ___
 1   41   54   10   13   20   47   8   43   48   29   19   42

___ ___   ___ ___ ___ ___ ___   ___ ___ ___ ___   ___ ___ ___
30   23   56   3   61   45   55   31   52   60   21   15   49   37

                                                                              "
                                                                              .
___ ___ ___   ___ ___ ___   ___ ___   ___ ___ ___ ___ ___
16   46   33   28   7   23   36   22   26   53   58   5   51

1. What instrument does a flautist play?

2. What word meaning understated comes from the Latin for 'below the cloth'?

3. What is a young kangaroo called?

4. In electronics, what name is given to a resistor that regulates a current by varying the resistance?

5. What unit of measurement is equal to 0.3048 meters?

6. What pale, bluish feldspar mineral and gemstone appears in the title of an 1868 mystery novel by Wilkie Collins?

7. According to the proverb, what is "wasted on the young"?

8. What is the frilled skirt worn by a ballerina called?

9. Which of the traditional seven deadly sins has the longest name?

10. What word can precede Land in the name of a region of the Middle East, and See to give an alternative name for the Vatican City?

11. What is a decorative ornament atop the point of a roof or tower called?

¹F	²L	³U	⁴T	⁵E

6	7	8	9	10	11

12	13	14	15

16	17	18	19	20	21	22	23

22	23	24	25

26	27	28	29	30	31	32	33	34

35	36	37	38	39

40	41	42	43

44	45	46	47	48	49	50	51

52	53	54	55

56	57	58	59	60	61

The answers to the clues on the right here contain **all but one** of the same letters as the clues on the left. Solve the clues, then write this unused letter in the middle circle to spell out—reading down the middle—something you might have time for now that you're retired. The first set has already been solved for you to give you an idea...

1. Graceful white waterbird

SWAN

Ⓝ

Used to be

WAS

2. Soil

Stag, male deer

3. Local climate conditions

Warm again

4. Band of classical musicians

Nuclear plants

5. Cowl

Homer Simpson's catchphrase

6. Fred Flintstone's neighbor

Long for

7. Prickly plant

Polished limestone

8. Japanese capital

Pinched, seized

Here's another tricky word jumble to keep you busy!
On each line here, two answers have been mixed together
and their letters placed in alphabetical order between them.
Can you unjumble the two answers in each case? The first has
been solved for you to make a start.

FRASIER   **SEINFIELD**

1. 1990s sitcoms
ADEEEFFIILNRRSS

2. Hitchcock horrors
BCDEHHIOPRSSTY

3. Birds of Prey
CDELNOORRTUUV

4. Batman villains
ACEEFGINNOPTUW

5. Team sports
AABBCEEHKKLLOSTY

6. Planets
AEENNNPRSTUUU

Starting at the 2 in the top left corner of the grid, can you complete all the squares in this number puzzle, using each of the calculations to fill in the gaps? Some of the answers have already been filled in to give you a start.

2 +6		÷ 4		+10 **12**
+ 4	X 2		+ 30		– 6
	+10	**16**	x 2		-26	
X 2		÷ 4		÷ 4		x 3
	÷ 3		+ 4		+ 10	**18**
÷ 4		+ 9		+ 18		+ 5
3	+ 10		x 2		– 3	

The names of three 10–letter fruits have been split up into five pairs of neighboring letters, and jumbled up below. Can you correctly rejoin the pairs to rebuild the original words?

AL   CA   EB   EL   ER

GO   NT   ON   OS   OU

PE   RM   RY   TE   WA

_____

_____

_____

You might think learning a new language is easier in childhood—Kids seem to pick up everything so much faster than adults, after all! But research has actually suggested that in some way adults make better learners, because they can use tried and trusted learning and memorization techniques—and, after a lifetime of missteps and embarrassments, aren't quite so afraid of making a mistake! If you have learning a language on your retirement to-do list, perhaps you have one of these in mind?

```
S  H  J  A  V  A  N  E  S  E  H  T  I  F  P  O  Y
W  S  S  N  H  C  E  Z  C  Y  S  A  C  F  O  N  P
A  O  B  I  A  F  O  A  N  A  I  G  E  W  R  O  N
H  C  D  B  K  I  A  E  Z  F  D  A  L  D  T  B  A
I  I  W  A  U  R  S  U  J  L  E  L  A  H  U  I  V
L  S  N  R  B  E  U  S  F  R  W  O  N  S  G  N  A
I  O  D  D  N  H  Y  T  U  A  S  G  D  I  U  D  J
S  U  F  A  I  G  L  Z  C  R  C  C  I  L  E  O  O
N  P  P  F  F  R  E  N  C  H  E  I  C  O  S  N  G
I  A  H  T  L  E  K  O  R  E  A  N  B  P  E  E  E
J  O  I  V  I  E  T  N  A  M  E  S  E  A  K  S  R
N  L  Y  L  N  K  M  A  N  D  A  R  I  N  R  I  M
A  A  W  J  A  I  R  I  S  H  D  U  T  C  H  A  A
Y  W  M  G  Z  T  E  A  S  P  A  N  I  S  H  N  N
U  K  R  A  I  N  I  A  N  H  F  I  N  N  I  S  H
```

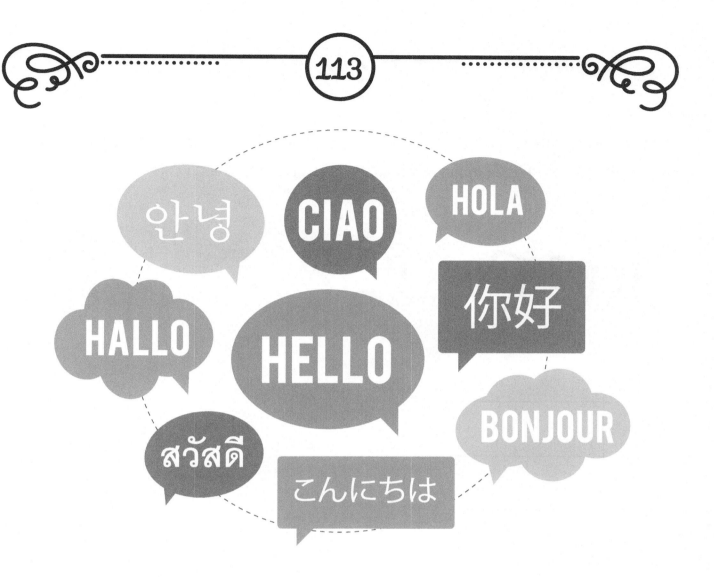

ARABIC   CZECH   DUTCH   FINNISH   FLEMISH
FRENCH   GERMAN   GREEK   HINDI   ICELANDIC
INDONESIAN   IRISH   ITALIAN   JAPANESE
JAVANESE   KOREAN   MANDARIN   NAVAJO
NORWEGIAN   POLISH   PORTUGUESE   RUSSIAN
SPANISH   SWAHILI   SWEDISH   TAGALOG   THAI
TURKISH   UKRAINIAN   URDU   VIETNAMESE

All the answers to these clues can be made from the letters in the word RECREATION. Can you answer them all?

_____ **1.** Sure, definite (7)

_____ **2.** Three-pointed hat (7)

_____ **3.** 1997 Nicolas Cage thriller (3, 3)

_____ **4.** More proximate (6)

_____ **5.** Transparent cover of the eye (6)

_____ **6.** Tidier (6)

_____ **7.** Oak seed (5)

_____ **8.** Fee paid for legal services (8)

_____ **9.** Fabrication, manufacture (8)

_____ **10.** Lay of the land (7)

Time for one last trip down the library.
Unscramble these classic American stories.

WHELP LOOSELY

NEW LAD

TELL ATHLETE HATER

HENCE-FORTH WET RUTS

MELT TOWLINE

THE STREETCAR TELL

Complete the grid so that each line and column,
and each 9x9 square, contains the numbers 1–9.

3							1	
	7		1		6			2
					7	8		
	8	6	3					
		2						
				4	9			7
				2		1		4
5			8					
6					5			

In this crossword, all the answers are anagrams of the clues. If there's more than one possibility, you'll have to make sure you pick the right one!

ACROSS

1. TRADE **4.** GEAR **6.** INTRO **7.** HEWN **8.** IGNORANCES
13. LEGO **15.** ROOTS **16.** TANG **17.** SHOES

DOWN

1. INCUT **2.** RETAX **3.** PRODS **4.** WAR **5.** GENRE **9.** GROAN
10. HEART **11.** COINS **12.** STAGE **14.** ATE

Let's take the last of our adventures abroad! Can you correctly name all 10 of the African countries numbered on the map below?

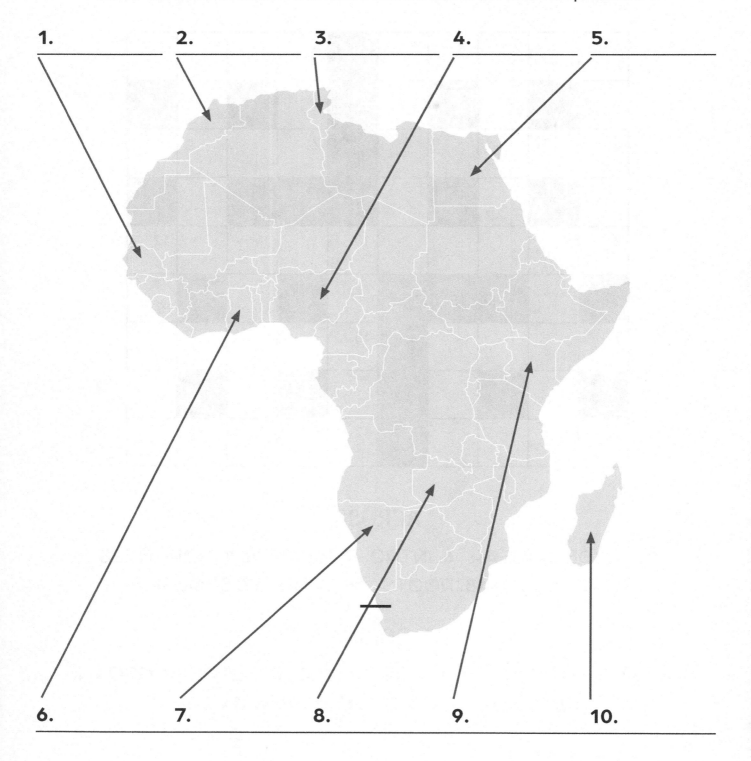

1. _____
2. _____
3. _____
4. _____
5. _____

6. _____
7. _____
8. _____
9. _____
10. _____

You've earned a glass of something strong!

Can you find your way through the maze to whisky on the other side?

Without a day job to go to, one day can easily slide into the next! So let's keep ourselves on track... Match the date on the left to the month in which it takes place on the right. The first answer has been filled in already to give you a head start...

1. President's Day	**A.** January
2. Labor Day	**B.** February
3. Columbus Day	**C.** April
4. Memorial Day	**D.** May
5. Summer Solstice	**E.** June
6. Fool's Day	**F.** July
7. Veterans' Day	**G.** September
8. US Independence Day	**H.** October
9. New Year's Eve	**I.** November
10. Martin Luther King, Jr. Day	**J.** December

One last word jumble to pit your wits against... On each line here, two answers have been mixed together and their letters placed in alphabetical order between them. Can you unjumble the two answers in each case? The first has been solved for you to make a start.

BLANKET

QUILT

1. Bedcovers
ABEIKLLNQTTU

2. Public transport
AABMRSTUWY

3. Prime numbers
EEEEEEHINNNRSTTTV

4. TV medical dramas
EEEEEHHLORSSSTUW

5. NBA teams
BCCEILLLSSTU

6. Greek letters
AAAEGHLMOP

ACROSS

7 Cools (6)

8 Instigate (6)

9 Vomit (4)

10 Mourned (8)

11 Flower seller (7)

13 Annoyances (5)

15 Dog (5)

17 Renter's agreement (7)

20 Stocky (8)

21 Creep forward (4)

23 Word used in a polite request (6)

24 Does well (6)

DOWN

1 Bloke, man (4)

2 Not as fast (6)

3 Inadequate, futile (7)

4 Feather (5)

5 Yellow pear–like fruit (6)

6 Combining many styles (8)

12 Legal trick that allows someone to escape punishment (8)

14 Water boilers (7)

16 Sweet liquid produced by plants (6)

18 Each (6)

19 Valuable business commodity (5)

22 Contact by phone (4)

There's a famous saying that says retirement isn't when you stop working, it's when you... what? Put the answers to these quiz questions in the corresponding rows in the grid to reveal the rest of the quotation by reading down the shaded column!

1.		M			
2.					Y
3.	N				
4.			S		
5.					
6.	I				
7.		I			
8.				I	
9.					E
10.	S				R
11.			M		
12.	E				
13.					
14.		O			
15.				O	
16.			I		
17.				I	
18.		D			
19.				A	
20				A	

1. Whose strength was lost when his hair was cut?

2. In what sci–fi film does a scientist turn into an insect after using a teleportation device? (3,3)

3. What is the part of a plant's stamen that contains the pollen called?

4. Perm is a city in what country?

5. What is Scotland's traditional plaid fabric called?

6. What tree has a variety called "weeping"?

7. *Food, Glorious Food* is song from what musical?

8. What animal lives in a warren?

9. Timpani are also known as what kind of drum?

10. What line on a weather map links places with the same air pressure?

11. What name links *The Walking Dead* star Reedus and the American painter and artist Rockwell?

12. Every English king from 1714–1830 had what name?

13. On what continent is Lake Tanganyika?

14. Which of Jesus' disciples was also known as Didymus?

15. In Charles Dickens' *A Tale of Two Cities*, the two cities in question are Paris and where?

16. What two-word phrase for a fashionable young woman was first popularly used for the silent movie star Clara Bow in 1971 (2,4)?

17. Which Ancient Greek poet wrote the *Aeneid*?

18. What halogen element is used in medicine as an antiseptic to swab wounds?

19. What is the northernmost country in mainland Europe?

20. What language would be spoken in a "teutonophone" country?

We're almost at the finish line! Time to take your foot off the gas a little with this puzzle dedicated to rest and relaxation.

```
W I N D D O W N A Z V E G O U T I
C H I L L O U T U N C L E N C H E
C H I L L A X Y S A E T I E K A T
S I T B A C K L N N W O D E I L A
O E P T A H R U O Y P U G N A H R
T S P U N E S O O L F F O E S A E
D S L A C K E N Z O E U T R P N P
T E R E L A X A E G N A E P R G U
I R Q U I E T E N B I C L U A L C
M T D N I W N U U R L G O T W O E
E S O P E R O T U I E E A E L O R
O E C D F L T X N N E E F L U S S
F D C T G O U E F S S L K D O E C
F C H R N L A Z E N W O D W O L S
P U T E E F R U O Y T U P I N L L
```

CHILL OUT   CHILLAX   DE-STRESS   EASE OFF   HANG LOOSE   HANG UP YOUR HAT
IDLE   LAZE   LET UP   LIE DOWN   LOAF   LOLL   LOOSEN UP   LOUNGE
LUXURIATE   PUT YOUR FEET UP   QUIETEN   RECLINE   RECUPERATE   RELAX
REPOSE   SIT BACK   SLACKEN   SLOW DOWN   SNOOZE   SPRAWL   TAKE IT EASY
TIME OFF   UNBUTTON   UNCLENCH   UNWIND   VEG OUT   WIND DOWN

Okay, you've earned this! Can you find your way through the maze to glass of red on the other side?

Conclusion

And that, as they say, is that!

Congratulations! You've reached the end of your Retirement Activity Book! Hopefully after solving all 125 of these puzzles and quizzes over the last hundred or so pages, you've taxed your gray matter a little, learnt a thing or two along the way, and happily spent even just a little bit of all this time you have spare now.

But in the words of the legendary television host Fred Rogers, "Often when you think you're at the end of something, you're at the beginning of something else."

So what next? A new hobby? A new language? Or how about another puzzle book...?

Hey—there's an open road ahead of you, after all!

Solutions

1

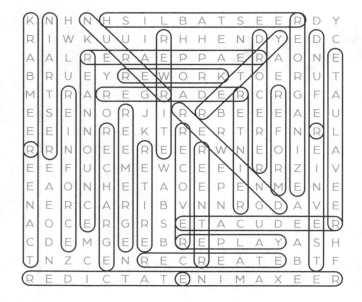

2

1. OREGON
2. NEWMAN
3. ELIJAH
4. BALTIC
5. URANUS
6. TAYLOR
7. ITALIC
8. TENNIS
9. WHITBY
10. INCHES
11. LENNOX
12. LISBON
13. TWELVE
14. ALFRED
15. KIDNEY
16. EEYORE
17. TRUMAN
18. HANDEL
19. EUROPE
20. MARTHA
21. ANDREW
22. LONDON
23. LUDWIG
24. DUBLIN
25. ANUBIS
26. YELLOW

Hidden answer: **"One — but it will take them all day!"**

3

1. Termite
2. Trireme
3. Merit
4. Meter
5. Miner
6. Reenter
7. Ermine
8. Mitten
9. Trite
10. Renter

4

Back to the drawing board

5

1. Apple, Pale = P
2. East, Set = A
3. Simple, Impel = S
4. Mars, Ram = S
5. Sample, Meals = P
6. Oregano, Orange = O
7. Drum, Mud = R
8. Texas, Axes = T

Solution: **PASSPORT**

6

1. Cuckoo
2. Candle
3. Grandfather
4. Church
5. Water

Missing link: **They are all types of clock**

7

1. *Gone with the Wind*
2. *The Bell Jar*
3. *Huckleberry Finn*
4. *Moby-Dick*
5. *The Grapes of Wrath*
6. *Beloved*

8

Ornithologist – Birds
Philatelist – Stamps
Cruciverbalist – Crosswords
Phillumenist – Matchboxes
Vexillologist – Flags
Oenophile – Wine
Bibliophile – Books
Numismatist – Coins
Toxophilite – Archery
Audiophile – Music

9

Correct answers: Ibsen, Nichols, Terence, Orton, Toller, Housman, Euripides, Williams, O'Neill, Odets, Diderot, Strindberg
Hidden answer: INTO THE WOODS

10

9	8	6	2	3	4	5	7	1
7	4	2	6	1	5	8	3	9
5	3	1	7	9	8	2	4	6
8	7	9	3	4	1	6	2	5
1	2	5	8	7	6	3	9	4
3	6	4	9	5	2	7	1	8
4	1	3	5	8	7	9	6	2
2	9	8	1	6	3	4	5	7
6	5	7	4	2	9	1	8	3

11

ALARM CLOCK
NIGHTSTAND
PILLOWCASE

12

13

1. France, Crane = F
2. Wilderness, Weirdness = L
3. Latrine, Relation = O
4. Writhe, White = R
5. Impale, Maple = I
6. Android, Ordain = D
7. Marine, Miner = A
Solution: **FLORIDA**

14

5	x3	15	+10	25	√	5
+3		−4		−9		+3
8	+3	11	+5	16	÷2	8
x2		+9		+12		−1
16	+4	20	+8	28	÷4	7
√		x2		+2		x3
4	x10	40	−10	30	−9	21

15

16

Up to speed

17

There are eight hexagons in total—including the entire shape!

18

PHOTOCOPIER
WATER COOLER

19

1	4	2	5	6	8	7	3	9
9	7	8	3	1	4	5	2	6
3	6	5	7	9	2	8	1	4
6	5	9	8	2	7	3	4	1
8	2	3	6	4	1	9	7	5
7	1	4	9	3	5	6	8	2
5	3	1	4	7	9	2	6	8
2	9	6	1	8	3	4	5	7
4	8	7	2	5	6	1	9	3

20

1. HONOLULU		11. LINGERIE
2. IGLESIAS		12. LABRADOR
3. SATURDAY		13. TRUEGRIT
4. WILLIAMS		14. IRISHSEA
5. INTERPOL		15. MAGELLAN
6. FEBRUARY		16. ELDORADO
7. EGYPTIAN		17. JANEEYRE
8. SALZBURG		18. OKLAHOMA
9. FALSTAFF		19. BABERUTH
10. UMBRELLA		

Hidden answer: **"His wife's full-time job!"**

21

Stellenbosch – South Africa
Niagara – Canada
Pisco Atacama – Chile
Napa Valley – USA
Beaujolais – France
Castile e León – Spain
Mendoza – Argentina
Chianti – Italy
Rheingau – Germany
Aguascalientes – Mexico

22

Correct answers: Paperback Writer, All My Loving, In My Life, Norwegian Wood, Tomorrow Never Knows, I Feel Fine, Taxman, Blackbird, Let It Be, All You Need is Love, Can't Buy Me Love, Kansas City

Hidden Answer: **Paint It Black**

23

C	O	N	T	E	X	T		E	X	T	R	A
	U		H		I			M		U		F
A	G	R	E	E		M		P		X		T
	H		I		O	B	S	O	L	E	T	E
S	T	A	R	K		E		W		D		R
I			S		F	R	E	E	F	O	R	M
T		S		I		R		S				A
U	L	T	I	M	A	T	E		P			T
A		A		P		H		F	I	N	C	H
T	A	D	P	O	L	E	S		C		R	
I		I		N			N		I	N	L	A	W
O		U		E		C			I		W	
N	O	M	A	D		E	X	A	C	T	L	Y

24

Burn the midnight oil

25

1. Relies
2. Reuse
3. Lieu
4. Sure
5. Riles
6. Rules
7. Eels
8. Lures
9. Leis
10. Reels

26

28

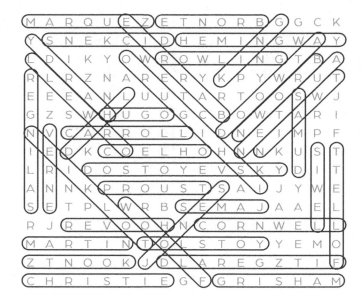

27

1. Random, Roman = D
2. Espanol, Planes = O
3. Water, Tear = W
4. Bing, Big = N
5. Towed, Owed = T
6. Airport, Parrot = I
7. Meantime, Matinee = M
8. Delays, Sadly = E

Solution: **DOWNTIME**

29

1. Bishop, Queen
2. Ostrich, Penguin
3. Brie, Camembert
4. Bogotá, Rio de Janeiro
5. Foxtrot, Quadrille
6. Claudius, Hadrian

30

BLACK HILLS
CRATER LAKE
EVERGLADES

31

8	1	2	6	5	4	7	3	9
5	3	6	9	1	7	8	4	2
4	9	7	8	3	2	1	5	6
3	7	9	2	8	5	4	6	1
2	5	4	7	6	1	3	9	8
6	8	1	4	9	3	5	2	7
1	4	8	5	2	9	6	7	3
9	6	5	3	7	8	2	1	4
7	2	3	1	4	6	9	8	5

32

1. Brazil
2. UK
3. Greece
4. India
5. South Africa
6. Argentina
7. Jamaica
8. Australia

33

H	E	M	S			P	H	A	R	A	O	H	S
O		A		E		O		E		R			O
M	I	S	C	A	S	T		G	U	A	R	D	
E		O		V			I		C			A	
S	E	N	S	E	O	F	S	M	E	L	L		
P			S		I		E		E		P		
U	R	N		D	O	Z	E	N		S	I	R	
N		E		R		Z		T				E	
	A	E	R	O	D	Y	N	A	M	I	C	S	
S		D		P			L		D			E	
C	H	I	M	P		G	A	L	L	E	O	N	
A		N		E		N		Y		A		T	
R	I	G	O	R	O	U	S		A	L	A	S	

34

Misery – Kathy Bates
The Hunt for Red October – Sean Connery
Jaws – Roy Scheider
Jurassic Park – Sam Neill
Alien – Sigourney Weaver
The Talented Mr Ripley – Matt Damon
Dog Day Afternoon – Al Pacino
Doubt – Meryl Streep

35

1. Iceland
2. Ireland
3. Norway
4. Denmark
5. Austria
6. Portugal
7. Belgium
8. Italy
9. Greece
10. Cyprus

36

Think outside the box

37

5	3	9	8	4	6	1	2	7
2	4	8	1	9	7	6	3	5
7	6	1	3	5	2	4	8	9
9	1	5	4	2	8	3	7	6
4	8	7	6	3	5	9	1	2
6	2	3	7	1	9	8	5	4
8	9	6	2	7	1	5	4	3
3	5	2	9	8	4	7	6	1
1	7	4	5	6	3	2	9	8

38

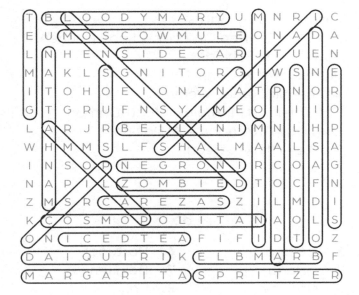

39

40

1. Fear, Ear = F
2. Robin, Born = I
3. Marinas, Airman = S
4. Hardy, Yard = H
5. Indigo, Dingo = I
6. Crown, Crow = N
7. Pig, Pi = G

41

1. Denim
2. Owned
3. Minted
4. Twine
5. Mine
6. Tine
7. Newt
8. Midtown
9. Dome
10. Mown
11. Toned
12. Monde

42

9	x 3	27	+ 3	30	÷ 10	3
+ 8		–7		–16		+ 6
17	+ 3	20	–6	14	–5	9
– 2		–12		+10		√
15	- 7	8	x 3	24	÷ 8	3
÷ 3		+2		–3		+ 4
5	+ 5	10	+ 11	21	÷ 3	7

43

1. BELIZE	9. GUITAR	17. NIMITZ
2. EDWARD	10. HAVANA	18. OSWALD
3. ICARUS	11. TENNIS	19. TARZAN
4. NAVAJO	12. DONALD	20. HILTON
5. GERMAN	13. OXFORD	21. IMELDA
6. CALVIN	14. INDIAN	22. NEWARK
7. ALMOND	15. NELSON	23. GEORGE
8. UPDIKE	16. GEMINI	

Hidden answer: **"Being caught doing nothing!"**

44

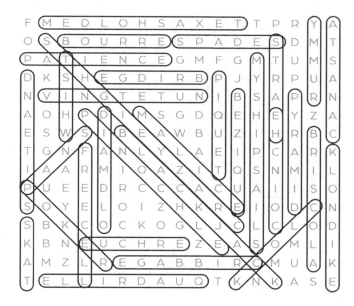

45

Correct answers: Nutmeg, Oak, Redwood, Willow, Aspen, Yew, Sycamore, Poplar, Rowan, Umbrella, Conifer, Elm
Hidden answer: **Norway spruce**

46

KINGFISHER
MEADOWLARK
ROADRUNNER

47

8	7	2	5	9	4	3	6	1
1	4	6	2	3	8	5	7	9
3	9	5	6	7	1	8	2	4
6	2	9	1	4	3	7	8	5
5	3	1	7	8	6	4	9	2
4	8	7	9	2	5	6	1	3
2	5	8	4	6	9	1	3	7
7	1	3	8	5	2	9	4	6
9	6	4	3	1	7	2	5	8

48

Players in a quintet = Four
Stars on the flag of Australia = Six
Square root of 9 = Three
Sides on a nonagon = Nine
Moons of Mars = Two
Cyclops' eyes = One
Bones in the human neck = Seven
Biblical Plagues of Egypt = Ten
Notes in an octave = Eight
V in Roman numerals = Five

49

M	E	A	T		F	R	E	Q	U	E	N	T
A		T		T		E		U		X		E
K	E	T	C	H	U	P		E	X	P	E	L
E		I		A		U		E		E		L
S	E	C	O	N	D	T	O	N	O	N	E	
U			K		E		C		S			C
R	I	P	O	F	F		P	O	M	E	L	O
E		R		U		G		N				N
	R	E	P	L	E	N	I	S	H	I	N	G
O		C		N		O		O		N		E
G	R	E	B	E		M	A	R	A	C	A	S
R		D		S		O		T		U		T
E	V	E	N	S	O	N	G		A	R	M	S

50

9	7	6	1	8	4	3	5	2
2	8	5	3	6	9	1	7	4
1	4	3	2	5	7	9	6	8
7	5	1	6	9	2	4	8	3
4	6	2	5	3	8	7	1	9
3	9	8	7	4	1	5	2	6
6	1	4	9	2	5	8	3	7
5	2	9	8	7	3	6	4	1
8	3	7	4	1	6	2	9	5

51

Back to square one

52

53

1. Ghost, Shot = G
2. Kale, Elk = A
3. Garment, Magnet = R
4. Cardio, Cairo = D
5. Waned, Dawn = E
6. China, Chia = N
7. Abridge, Badger = I
8. Channel, Chanel = N
9. Granite, Retina = G
Solution: **GARDENING**

54

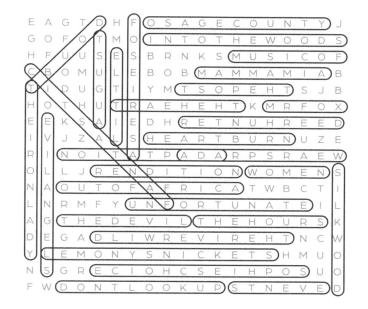

55

1. Shark
2. Uptown
3. Toto
4. Tongue
5. Monsoon
6. Janitor
7. Eighty
8. Yogi
9. Aardvark
10. Dido
11. Wife

Hidden answer: **"I enjoy waking up and not having to go to work. So, I do it three or four times a day."**

56

1. Cappuccino
2. Long black
3. Latte
4. Espresso
5. Cortado
6. Mocha
7. Americano
8. Macchiato
9. Flat white
10. Decaf
11. Frappe

57

1. Cello, Violin
2. Cube, Cylinder
3. Butterfly, Crawl
4. Java, Hokkaido
5. Comma, Semicolon
6. Oregano, Thyme

58

1. Absent
2. Hastens
3. Haunt
4. Butane
5. Abets
6. Hates
7. Sunhat
8. Unseats
9. Beta
10. Etna

59

ODOMETER   RADIATOR   TAILPIPE

60

	D		M		R		O		F		H	
B	E	C	A	M	E		C	A	L	L	E	D
	L		D		D		E		O		C	
W	E	E	D		A	L	A	C	R	I	T	Y
	T		E		C		N		A		I	
N	E	O	N	A	T	E		S	L	I	C	K
	A				S		C			N		
M	A	K	E	R		S	H	R	I	N	K	S
	I		A		S		E		M		L	
P	R	E	S	E	N	C	E		P	L	A	Y
	M		I		O		T		A		X	
W	A	L	L	O	W		A	B	L	O	O	M
	N		Y		S		H		E		N	

61

1. HALIFAX
2. ISOTOPE
3. HANCOCK
4. OCTOBER
5. NABOKOV
6. EXTINCT
7. YANKEES
8. IRELAND
9. MESSAGE
10. HEPBURN
11. OYSTERS
12. MADONNA
13. EVEREST
14. FRIENDS
15. OMICRON
16. RICHARD
17. ELECTRA
18. VACCINE
19. EARHART
20. RAINMAN

Hidden answer: **"Hi honey, I'm home — forever!"**

62

Novak Djokovic = Tennis
Lionel Messi = Soccer
Tom Watson = Golf
Kevin Durant = Basketball
Lewis Hamilton = Formula 1
Manny Pacquiao = Boxing
Maurice Greene = Athletics
Ryan Murphy = Swimming
Katie Zaferes = Triathlon
Simone Biles = Gymnastics

63

1. Lincoln
2. Wilson
3. Arthur
4. Garfield
5. Ford

Missing Link: **They're all the names of US Presidents**

64

6	3	2	8	9	4	1	5	7
8	5	7	3	1	6	4	2	9
1	4	9	2	7	5	6	8	3
7	9	4	6	5	3	8	1	2
2	8	3	1	4	9	7	6	5
5	1	6	7	2	8	3	9	4
4	7	1	9	8	2	5	3	6
9	6	8	5	3	7	2	4	1
3	2	5	4	6	1	9	7	8

65

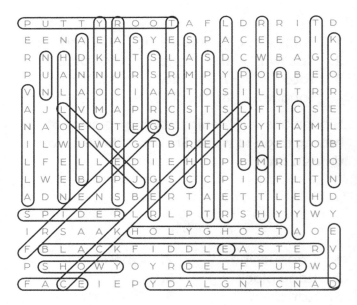

66

1. Thigh, High = T
2. Radish, Shard = I
3. Sample, Pleas = M
4. Easter, Stare = E
5. Chests, Chess = T
6. Naïve, Vine = A
7. Brides, Dries = B
8. Local, Coal = L
9. Yokels, Yolks = E

Solution: **TIMETABLE**

67

1. *Ethan Frome*
2. *The Great Gatsby*
3. *East of Eden*
4. *White Fang*
5. *On the Road*
6. *The Color Purple*

68

(Get your) foot in the door

69

1. Peru
2. Colombia
3. Venezuela
4. Brazil
5. Bolivia
6. Chile
7. Argentina
8. Uruguay

70

71

Correct answers: Pozole, Ukha, Minestrone, Pho, Escudella, Ramen, Navarin, Irish, Coq au vin, Kare-kare, Étouffée, Lancashire hotpot

Hidden answer: **PUMPERNICKEL**

72

7	x 2	14	+ 6	20	÷ 4	5
+ 5		+ 6		+ 1		+ 2
12	+ 8	20	+ 1	21	÷ 3	7
x 3		÷ 5		– 13		+ 9
36	÷ 9	4	x 2	8	x 2	16
+ 4		+ 6		x 4		÷ 4
40	÷ 4	10	+ 22	32	÷ 8	4

74

C	H	U	C	K	L	E	■	M	I	N	O	R
U	■	R	■	I	■	N	A	■	I	■	E	
B	R	A	I	N	■	G	A	D	G	E	T	S
E	■	N	■	G	I	E	■	C	■	O		
D	R	I	L	L	I	N	G	■	S	E	A	L
■	U	E	■	E	K	■	V					
C	O	M	B	A	T	■	U	N	A	B	L	E
L	■	R	P	U	A	■						
O	A	T	S	■	B	R	A	C	E	L	E	T
S	I	F	A	K	L	O						
E	A	G	E	R	L	Y	L	E	A	R	N	
S	H	E	E	E	D	E						
T	I	T	L	E	■	R	E	S	I	S	T	S

73

P A E G C T R O P R I A K M A O Y
A K F N T F O R E S T A U R A N T
L A B A I U I K Z A Y B S T O B M N
A C O C P O J J F U T E G S T O U N
C T P G U A T S U A N T E N U S
E H O R D A M L C D H K I R T
O I G F W L E B H N C A Y N T E
H O T K N E S E W A R D Y M A B E
O U D A A R I K G J D Y M I I N T
T R E E Y U I M E I E I I Z B U E
E H R R P R H I Y M Z B U E N F O
L B I L C O C K T A I L S L U S O
G N I L L E K R O N S W A F I D
N A T I O N A L P A R K S Z J I
G A R D E N R N A N I R A M J L I

75

COMPUTER
KEYBOARD
WIRELESS

76

1. Gander
2. Enraging
3. Dagger
4. Earning
5. Ending
6. Ginger
7. Grading
8. Grinned
9. Grande
10. Danger

77

Heretofore = Previously
Acrimony = Spite
Capricious = Unpredictable
Zephyr = Breeze
Verisimilitude = Truth
Draconian = Ruthless
Pulchritudinous = Beautiful
Sagacious = Wise
Selcouth = Bizarre
Predilection = Fondness

78

1. Dragon, Mermaid
2. Sleeping bag, Tent
3. Potato, Turnip
4. Aegean, Mediterranean
5. Diamond, Strike
6. Casino, Taxi Driver

79

1. April, Pair = L
2. Abacus, Scuba = A
3. Pinter, Petri = N
4. Tangier, Retain = G
5. Dueting, Tinged = U
6. Hating, Thing = A
7. Gang, Nag = G
8. Pierce, Price = E
SOLUTION: **LANGUAGE**

80

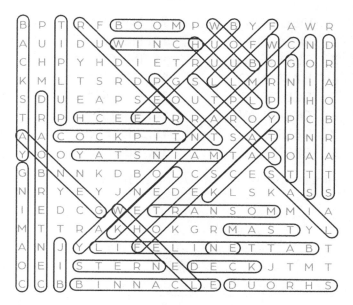

81

4	2	9	6	8	7	3	5	1
7	8	1	3	5	9	6	2	4
5	6	3	4	2	1	8	7	9
1	7	2	5	3	8	4	9	6
9	3	4	1	7	6	2	8	5
6	5	8	2	9	4	7	1	3
8	4	6	9	1	2	5	3	7
3	9	7	8	6	5	1	4	2
2	1	5	7	4	3	9	6	8

82

1. RE
2. IRE
3. TIRE
4. TRIER
5. RETIRE
6. REWRITE
7. WATERIER
8. FIREWATER

83

1. OEDIPUS
2. FLORIDA
3. THOREAU
4. HARVARD
5. ECUADOR
6. OHMSLAW
7. PAULING
8. EZEKIEL
9. NINEVEH
10. HEYJUDE
11. IMHOTEP
12. GOLDWYN
13. HADRIAN
14. WILLIAM
15. ANTIGUA
16. YELTSIN

Hidden answer: **"Of the open highway"**

86

84

F	O	R	E	W	A	R	N	E	D		A	
A		E		I		H		X			D	
C	A	P	O	N		O	U	T	C	O	M	E
T		L		E		D		E			I	
O	M	I	T		F	E	B	R	U	A	R	Y
R		C		G		S		N			E	
Y	E	A	R	L	Y		L	A	M	B	D	A
	X		I		G		L		R		A	F
S	C	I	S	S	O	R	S		H	A	L	F
	E		T		A		T		I		R	
B	R	I	B	E	R	Y		H	E	L	L	O
	P		N		E		I		L		L	N
	T		A	S	T	R	I	N	G	E	N	T

85

There are 16 squares in total.

87

3	2	5	8	4	6	1	9	7
4	6	8	1	7	9	3	2	5
9	1	7	2	3	5	4	8	6
7	3	6	4	1	8	9	5	2
2	5	9	7	6	3	8	4	1
8	4	1	9	5	2	6	7	3
1	8	2	3	9	7	5	6	4
6	7	3	5	8	4	2	1	9
5	9	4	6	2	1	7	3	8

88

EL SALVADOR
LUXEMBOURG
NEW ZEALAND

89

■	E	L	A	S	T	I	C	■
■	■	O	■	P	■	A	■	S
P	E	N	C	I	L	■	P	E	T
O	■	G	■	L	■	■	E	■
W	H	E	E	L	S	■	B	T
E	■	R	■	S	P	E	L	L	S
R	■	■	■	R	■	I	■	O
E	N	D	■	K	I	T	T	E	N
D	■	O	■	N	■	H	■
■	T	R	I	G	G	E	R	■

90

91

Armoire = Wardrobe
Jardinière = Plant pot
Canapé = Sofa
Console = Side table
Torchère = Candlestick
Bureau = Writing desk
Caquetoire = Armchair
Tallboy = Chest of drawers
Credenza = Sideboard
Four poster = Bed

92

1. Turkey
2. Russia
3. Kazakhstan
4. Mongolia
5. Japan
6. Saudi Arabia
7. United Arab Emirates
8. Sri Lanka
9. Cambodia
10. Philippines

93

Correct answers: Brownlow, Artful Dodger, Rokesmith, Nancy, Amy Dorrit, Bob Cratchit, Yawler, Raplh Nickleby, Uriah Heep, David Copperfield, Gradgrind, Ebenezer Scrooge
Hidden answer: **Barnaby Rudge**

94

1. Brunch, Churn = B
2. Equator, Quatre = O
3. Reasons, Snares = O
4. Stoking, Ingots = K
5. Pitch, Pith = C
6. Flour, Four = L
7. Tsunami, Mantis = U
8. Ribs, Sir = B

SOLUTION: **BOOKCLUB**

95

10	÷ 2	5	+ 7	12	x 2	24
–4		x 3		+ 4		÷ 6
6	+ 9	15	+ 1	16	√	4
–2		+ 5		+12		x 6
4	x 5	20	+ 8	28	– 4	24
x 2		+ 4		–7		–17
8	x 3	24	–3	21	÷ 3	7

96

1. Aileron
2. Oxtail
3. Tailor
4. Retinol
5. Loiter
6. Inert
7. Ornate
8. Rationale
9. Aorta
10. Elation

97

M	A	N	E	D		R	A	C	E
A		O		A		A		O	
P	E	T	A	L		T	I	R	E
L		E		E			G		
E	N	D	O	S	C	O	P	I	C
	A				A		A		L
S	K	I	S		L	I	N	G	O
	E		I		M		E		U
E	D	I	T		S	O	L	I	D

98

	L		P		S		S	P	O	O	K	S
P	A	N	A	C	H	E		A		V		Y
	G		R		E		S	C	R	E	E	N
C	O	A	C	H	E	S		I		R		O
	O		E		P		I	N	S	T	E	P
I	N	C	L	U	D	I	N	G		U		S
N		O			O		E			R		I
H		L		E	G	G	P	L	A	N	T	S
A	L	A	R	M	S		T		S		A	
B		N		B		A	N	Y	T	I	M	E
I	N	D	I	A	N		E		R		P	
T		E		R		A	S	H	A	M	E	D
S	T	R	O	K	E		S		L		R	

99

100

DELPHINIUM   HELIOTROPE   SNAPDRAGON

101

2	3	4	9	5	1	8	6	7
5	1	8	4	6	7	2	9	3
6	9	7	2	3	8	5	1	4
8	7	6	3	1	4	9	5	2
4	5	1	6	2	9	3	7	8
3	2	9	8	7	5	1	4	6
1	8	5	7	4	2	6	3	9
9	4	3	1	8	6	7	2	5
7	6	2	5	9	3	4	8	1

102

Gregory Peck = To Kill a Mockingbird
Paul Newman = Cool Hand Luke
Richard Burton = Cleopatra
Audrey Hepburn = Sabrina
Barbra Streisand = Funny Girl
Robert Redford = Barefoot in the Park
Goldie Hawn = Cactus Flower
Jane Fonda = Cat Ballou
John Wayne = The Quiet Man
Bette Davis = All About Eve

103

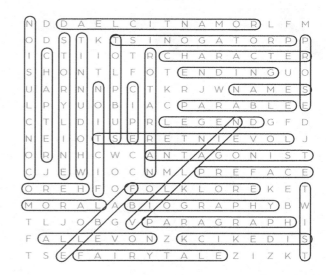

104

1.	YEAST	7.	ELLEN	13.	DELTA
2.	OUNCE	8.	ROYAL	14.	ALBUM
3.	UNCLE	9.	GENOA	15.	YEATS
4.	NORTH	10.	ELVIS	16.	ORION
5.	EGYPT	11.	THOSE	17.	FREUD
6.	VERNE	12.	AARON	18.	FEVER

Hidden answer: **"You never get a day off!"**

105

B	E	T	R	A	Y		S	T	U	D	Y	
O		R		N		C		O		I		T
B	R	A	V	A	D	O		D	I	S	C	O
C		C		G		N		A		D		K
A	C	T	O	R		C	R	Y	B	A	B	Y
T				A		E				I		O
	D	I	S	M	A	N	T	L	I	N	G	
A		N		T		A		A				S
V	I	N	T	N	E	R		W	O	R	S	T
O		A		U		A		S		E		I
W	O	R	L	D		T	O	U	R	I	S	T
S		D		G		E		I		G		C
	A	S	K	E	D		S	T	E	N	C	H

107

Correct answers: [The] Jungle Book, Up, Ratatouille, Aladdin, Sleeping Beauty, [The] Sword in the Stone, Inside Out, Cinderella, Pocahontas, [The] Aristocats, [The] Rescuers, Kung Fu Panda
Hidden answer: **Jurassic Park**

108

1. Flute
2. Subtle
3. Joey
4. Rheostat
5. Foot
6. Moonstone
7. Youth
8. Tutu
9. Gluttony
10. Holy
11. Finial

Coded answer: **"The goal is to enjoy it to the fullest, but not so fully that you run out of money."**

106

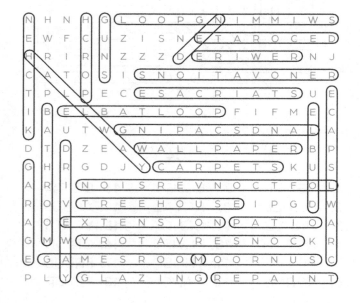

109

1. Swan, Was = N
2. Earth, Hart = E
3. Weather, Reheat = W
4. Orchestra, Reactors = H
5. Hood, D'oh = O
6. Barney, Yearn = B
7. Bramble, Marble = B
8. Tokyo, Took = Y

Solution: **NEW HOBBY**

110

1. *Frasier, Seinfeld*
2. *Psycho, The Birds*
3. Condor, Vulture
4. Penguin, Two Face
5. Basketball, Hockey
6. Neptune, Uranus

111

2	+6	8	÷ 4	2	+10	12
+ 4		x 2		+ 30		– 6
6	+10	16	x 2	32	-26	6
x 2		÷ 4		÷ 4		x 3
12	÷ 3	4	+ 4	8	+ 10	18
÷ 4		+ 9		+ 18		+ 5
3	+ 10	13	x 2	26	– 3	23

112

CANTALOUPE
GOOSEBERRY
WATERMELON

113

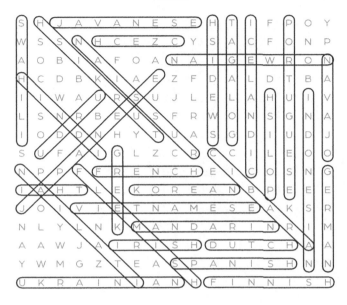

114

1. Certain
2. Tricorn
3. *Con Air*
4. Nearer
5. Cornea
6. Neater
7. Acorn
8. Retainer
9. Creation
10. Terrain

115

1. *Sleepy Hollow*
2. *Walden*
3. *The Tell-Tale Heart*
4. *The Turn of the Screw*
5. *Little Women*
6. *The Scarlet Letter*

116

3	6	8	4	9	2	7	1	5
4	7	5	1	8	6	3	9	2
2	1	9	5	3	7	8	4	6
7	8	6	3	5	1	4	2	9
9	4	2	7	6	8	5	3	1
1	5	3	2	4	9	6	8	7
8	9	7	6	2	3	1	5	4
5	2	1	8	7	4	9	6	3
6	3	4	9	1	5	2	7	8

117

T	R	E	A	D		R	A	G	E
U		X		R		A		R	
N	I	T	R	O		W	H	E	N
I		R		P			E		
C	O	A	R	S	E	N	I	N	G
	R			A		C		A	
O	G	L	E		R	O	O	S	T
	A		A		T		N		E
G	N	A	T		H	O	S	E	S

119

120

President's Day = February
Labor Day = September
Columbus Day = October
Memorial Day = May
Summer Solstice = June
Fool's Day = April
Veterans' Day = November
US Independence Day = July
New Year's Eve = December
Martin Luther King, Jr. Day = January

118

1. Senegal
2. Morocco
3. Tunisia
4. Nigeria
5. Egypt
6. Ghana
7. Namibia
8. Zambia
9. Kenya
10. Madagascar

121

1. Blanket, Quilt
2. Subway, Tram
3. Seventeen, Thirteen
4. House, St Elsewhere
5. Bulls, Celtics
6. Alpha, Omega

122

124

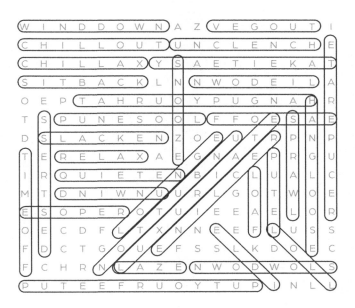

125

123

1. SAMSON
2. THEFLY
3. ANTHER
4. RUSSIA
5. TARTAN
6. WILLOW
7. OLIVER
8. RABBIT
9. KETTLE
10. ISOBAR
11. NORMAN
12. GEORGE
13. AFRICA
14. THOMAS
15. LONDON
16. ITGIRL
17. VIRGIL
18. IODINE
19. NORWAY
20. GERMAN

Hidden answer: **"Start working at living"**